Tugs and Offshore Supply Vessels
2006/07
(Baltic and Scandinavia)

by

James Dodds

Introduction

This listing of tugs and offshore supply ships owned or operated by companies based in countries bordering the Baltic and in Scandianvia follows up that published earlier in the year listing similar vessels owned or operated by companies based in the UK and Ireland. Not only are such vessels from these northern European countries visitng the UK in ever-increasing numbers but observers are travelling much further afield in order to see them.

As with all such lists of ships, no guarantee is given about the accuracy of the figures which should be considered merely as a guideline. Every effort has been made to obtain correct figures but there is sometimes disagreement among the main sources. We have tended to use figures given in *Lloyd's Register of Shipping* where these are available. For very new vessels, little information other than a name is available but some of these have been included in the fleets. Information has been corrected to the end of August 2005.

The details for each vessel are as follows
Column 1   Name and flag, followed by former names
Column 2   Year of build
Column 3   Gross tonnage
Coumnl 4   Length overall
Column 5   Beam
Column 6   Draught
Column 7   Horsepower
Column 8   Bollard pull ahead (n/a means not available or not applicable)

I wish to thank all the companies which have responded to requests for information, the vast majority of those listed having done so. I also wish to thank my father for his help, Dominic and Bernard McCall who have added further information, and Dag Bakka Jr, Bent Mikkelsen, Jan G Rautawaara and Jerzy Swieszkowski who have checked through, amended and updated many of the listings. Gilbert Mayes has once again checked many details and offered his help and advice. Thanks also to the staff at Sebright Printers for their excellent work.

Despite our best efforts, the book may contain errors. We have tried to use the correct national alphabets and lettering. A consequence of this is that the sequence of letters may be unexpected for British readers. So æ and ø will come at the end of the alphabet. Users of the book who have further information about any of the vessels listed are invited to contact me via the publisher.

James Dodds
Aberdeen, October 2005

Published by Bernard McCall, 400 Nore Road, Portishead, Bristol, BS20 8EZ, England.
Website : www.coastalshipping.co.uk
Telephone/fax : 01275 846178. E-mail : bernard@coastalshipping.co.uk
All distribution enquiries should be addressed to the publisher.

Printed by Sebright Printers, 12 - 18 Stokes Croft, Bristol, BS1 3PR
Telephone : 0117 942 5827; fax : 0117 942 0671;
e-mail : info@sebright.co.uk; website : www.sebright.co.uk

ISBN : 1-902953-21-5

Front cover : The HERAKLES working at Gdynia on 28 July 2002.

(Bernard McCall)

BOURBON OFFSHORE NORWAY AS

P.O. Box H, N-6099 Fosnavåg, Norway
Tel : +47 70 08 60 00   Fax : +47 70 08 60 01
E-mail : office@bourbon-offshore.no
Website : www.bourbon-online.com
Livery - Green hull with white band round the bow, white housing and funnel

BLUE ANGEL (BHS)	1999	3073	84,00	18,80	6,31	9592	n/a
(ex Havila Lista-03)							
BOURBON (tbn)	2006	3900	88,80	19,00	6,60		
BOURBON							
BORGSTEIN (NOR)	2003	3905	80,00	18,00	6,60	20000	237.0
(ex Havila Borgstein-03)							
BOURBON							
CHARISMA (NOR)	1999	2599	73,60	16,40	6,90	16200	190.0
(ex Havila Charisma-03)							
BOURBON							
CHARMER (NIS)	1991	1599	65,50	13,80	6,03	9700	125.0
(ex Havila Charmer-03; Torbas-98)							
BOURBON							
CHIEFTAIN (NIS)	1983	1598	68,35	15,60	6,44	12728	136.0
(ex Havila Chieftain-03; Rembas-98; Strilborg-93; Solfonn-93)							

The BOURBON CHIEFTAIN photographed outward bound from Portsmouth on 14 June 2005.
(Danny Lynch)

Name	Year						
BOURBON CROWN (NOR)	2001	3154	80,45	18,00	6,90	14400	202.0
(ex Havila Crown-03)							
BOURBON DOLPHIN	2006	2900	75,20	17,00	6,50	16320	180.0
BOURBON EKO (NOR)	1992	1673	63,00	15,00	5,50	5000	n/a
(ex Havila Eko-03; Rescue Eko-98)							
BOURBON EMERALD (NOR)	2004	3756	90,70	18,80	5,80	7352	n/a
BOURBON HIDRA (NOR)	1999	3102	84,60	18,80	6,31	9592	n/a
(ex Havila Hidra-03)							
BOURBON JADE (NOR)	2004	3963	90,70	18,80		9332	n/a
BOURBON OPALE	2004		90,70	18,80		9332	
BOURBON ORCA	2006		83,60	18,50	7,00	13600	180.0
BOURBON PERIDOT	2005		91,10	19,00	6,65		n/a
BOURBON SCOTIA (BHS)	1982	1948	67,47	16,79	6,10	6760	n/a
(ex Havila Scotia-03; Boa Scotia-98; Far Scotia-97; Seaforth Emperor-89)							
BOURBON SURF (NOR)	2003	3905	80,00	18,00	6,60	20000	237.0
(ex Havila Surf-03)							
BOURBON TAMPEN (NOR)	2002	3313	88,60	18,80	6,20	9928	n/a
(ex Havila Tampen-03)							
BOURBON TOPAZ (NOR)	2005	3745	86,20	19,00	6,65	5982	n/a

Offshore services worldwide
Subsidiary company of SURF, Marseille ; Groupe Bourbon

The BOTNICA at Peterhead.

(The late Keith Morgan)

FINNISH MARITIME ADMIN

Porkkalankatu 5, Fi-00180 Helsinki, Finland
Tel : +358 204 48 40   Fax : +358 204 48 4355
Website : www.fma.fi

Managed by Subsea 7 (Norway)

BOTNICA	(FIN)	1998	6370	96,70	24,00	8,50	20376	n/a
FENNICA	(FIN)	1993	9088	116,00	26,00	8,40	20400	234.0
NORDICA	(FIN)	1994	9088	116,00	26,00	8,40	20400	234.0

Icebreaking services in the Baltic in winter and offshore services in the North Sea in the summer

DOF MANAGEMENT AS

5392 Storebo, Norway
Tel : +47 56 18 10 00   Fax : +47 56 18 10 06
E-mail : management@dof.no
Website : www.dof.no
Livery - Red hull with white housing, wheelhouse and funnel with 'DOF' in blue letters

SKANDI	(tbn)	2006	3350	85,65	19,70			n/a
SKANDI ADMIRAL	(NOR)	1999	4370	83,30	20,50	7,80	27400	250.0
(ex Northern Admiral-03)								
SKANDI BARRA	(NOR)	2005	3350	86,00	19,70			n/a
SKANDI BERGEN	(NIS)	1987	2499	75,50	16,60	5,60	13200	170.0
(ex Far Scout-96)								
SKANDI BUCHAN	(NIS)	2002	3360	83,85	19,70	5,85	8208	n/a

The SKANDI BUCHAN arrives at Aberdeen on 4 August 2003.

(David Dodds)

SKANDI							
CALEDONIA (NOR)	2003	3285	83,85	19,70	6,00	4104	n/a
SKANDI CAPTAIN (NOR)	2004	2592	73,50	16,40	6,22	4080	n/a
SKANDI CARLA (BHS)	2001	4456	83,85	19,70	6,10	13404	n/a
SKANDI CHIEFTAIN (NIS)	2005	2592	74,30	16,40			n/a
SKANDI FALCON (NOR)	1990	2637	81,90	18,00	4,97	6600	n/a
SKANDI FJORD (BHS)	1983	3254	87,68	18,45	4,97	7200	
SKANDI FOULA (NOR)	2002	3252	83,85	19,70	5,85	8208	n/a
SKANDI HAV (NIS)	1983	2896	87,68	18,45	5,25	7200	n/a
SKANDI INSPECTOR (BHS)	1979	3345	81,10	18,03	4,97	4800	
SKANDI MARSTEIN (NOR)	1996	3171	83,70	19,70	5,85	7988	n/a
SKANDI MØGSTER (NIS)	1998	2598	73,75	16,40	6,90	15014	150.0
SKANDI NAVICA (IOM)	1999	6083	99,43	22,00	7,60	17130	
SKANDI PATAGONIA (NIS)	2000	4641	93,30	19,70	6,00	13880	
SKANDI RONA (NIS)	2002	3252	83,85	19,70	5,85	8208	n/a
SKANDI SOTRA (NOR)	2003	3482	83,85	19,70	6,10	9796	n/a
SKANDI STOLMEN (NOR)	1997	1969	67,06	16,00	6,00	5460	n/a
SKANDI STORD (NOR)	1999	2656	73,75	16,40	6,90	14800	180.0
SKANDI TEXEL	2006		69,30	16,40			n/a
SKANDI YARE (NIS)	2001	1970	67,00	16,00	6,00	5378	n/a
Managed for Redningsselskapet, Oslo							
SKANDI BETA (NOR)	1982	1751	67,86	14,50	5,01	10560	130.0
Managed for DOF BOA AS (Norway)							
SKANDI PMS I (CYM)	2002	4820	81,00	20,00	8,20	18400	200.0
(ex Boa Giant-04)							
SKANDI PMS II (CYM)	2002	4820	81,00	20,00	8,20	18400	200.0
(ex Boa Hercules-04)							

Offshore services worldwide. Also operate cable layers & well stimulation vessels

EIDESVIK AS

5443 Bømlo, Norway
Tel : +47 53 44 80 00   Fax : +47 53 44 80 01
E-mail : office@eidesvik.no
Website : www.eidesvik.no
Livery - Orange hull with white trim and large white 'E'; mustard housing and wheelhouse

SUBSEA VIKING (NOR)	1999	7401	103,00	22,00	7,85	14000	n/a
VIKING (tbn) (NOR)	2006	2602	73,40	16,60	6,50	5520	n/a
VIKING AVANT (NOR)	2004	3600	92,70	20,40	7,50	9248	n/a
VIKING DYNAMIC (NOR)	2002	3524	90,20	19,00	7,00	12745	n/a
VIKING ENERGY (NOR)	2002	4000	84,90	20,40	8,00	10460	n/a
VIKING NEREUS (NOR)	2004	2602	73,40	16,60	6,50	5520	n/a
VIKING POSEIDON (NOR)	1998	4718	93,35	22,00	7,05	10760	n/a
VIKING QUEEN (NOR)	1984	2295	75,04	16,01	7,40	12600	186.0
VIKING THAUMAS (NOR)	2005	2602	73,40	16,60	6,50	5520	
VIKING TROLL (NOR)	1984	2516	78,60	16,01	7,42	12560	150.0
(ex Kongstein-87)							

Managed for Eidsurf AS (Norway), owned jointly with SURF, Marseille

SURF VIKING	2003	2410	70,40	16,60	6,50	6572	n/a
VIKING SURF (NOR)	2002	2417	70,40	16,60	6,50	6572	n/a

Offshore services mainly in the Norwegian sector of North Sea

ESVAGT A/S

Adgangsvejen 1, DK-6700 Esbjerg, Denmark
Tel : +45 76 11 47 00   Fax : +45 76 11 47 05
E-mail : mail@esvagt.dk
Website : www.esvagt.dk
Livery - Dark red hull and housing with 'ESVAGT' on hull in large black letters

ESVAGT BRAVO (DIS)	1962/82	172	30,95	7,05	2,40	500	n/a
(ex Jane Brigit-81; Ulla Nord-78; Ulla Somand-74; Rex-70)							
ESVAGT CAPELLA (DIS)	2004	931	44,03	11,00	4,24	1917	15.0
ESVAGT CHARLIE (DIS)	1976/92	319	39,75	8,20	4,20	900	n/a
(ex Rutane-91)							
ESVAGT CONNECTOR (DIS) *	2000	1863	56,64	14,60	6,02	6520	95.0
(ex Faroe Connector-02; Esvagt Connector-01)							
ESVAGT CORONA (DIS)	2004	931	44,03	11,00	4,24	1917	15.0
ESVAGT DELTA (DIS)	1974/91	319	39,75	8,20	4,20	900	n/a
(ex Kapilsund-91)							
ESVAGT ECHO (DIS)	1962/62	217	34,13	6,60	3,00	497	n/a
(ex Gerda Grenius-83, Middlebank-80; Anna Vanggard-77; Skafto-74)							
ESVAGT GAMMA (DIS)	1985	1361	64,76	13,82	5,40	8640	110.0
(ex Smit-Lloyd 92-98; Atlantic Poseidon-85)							
ESVAGT KAPPA (DIS)	2002	830	47,10	11,00	6,30	2430	35.0
(ex BUE Gairsay-02)							
ESVAGT OBSERVER (DIS)	2000	1863	56,64	14,60	6,02	6520	95.0
ESVAGT OMEGA (DIS)	1976	1380	64,76	13,82	4,75	7040	91.0
(ex Omega 807-88; Seaforth Laird-87; Lovat Salvator-78)							
ESVAGT PRESERVER (DIS)	1966/83	269	37,56	6,75	3,40	498	n/a
(ex Preserver-91; Esvagt Delta-83; Lis Frank-82)							
ESVAGT PREVENTER (DIS)	1969/82	213	33,60	6,60	3,30	880	n/a
(ex Preventer-91; Subriellen-82; Tina Pantos-74)							
ESVAGT PROMOTOR (DIS)	1965/82	172	30,95	6,60	3,30	498	n/a
(ex Promotor-91; Esvagt Charlie-83; Henriette-82; Chatina-81; Jimmy-75; Pollux-72)							
ESVAGT PROTECTOR (DIS)	1969/82	213	33,60	6,60	3,30	880	n/a
(ex Protector-91; Havsvind-82; Marianne Bodker-81; Shika-72)							
ESVAGT SIGMA (DIS)	2002	830	47,10	11,00	6,30	2430	35.0
(ex BUE Orkney-02)							

* *On bareboat charter to Norwegian Coastguard and renamed KV CONNECTOR under Norwegian flag*

Offshore services in the North Sea and Irish Sea

Vessels in the ESVAGT fleet are distinguished by having their upperworks painted in the same deep red colour as the hull as seen in this view of the ESVAGT OBSERVER approaching Aberdeen on 8 November 2004.

(David Dodds)

FARSTAD SHIPPING ASA

Notenesgate 14, St. Olavs Plass, 6002 Ålesund, Norway
Tel : +47 70 12 44 60   Fax : +47 70 12 85 30
E-mail : post@farstad.no
Website : www.farstad.no
Livery - Red hull with large white 'F'; white housing & wheelhouse

FAR CENTURION (IOM)	1983	1599	67,72	15,88	6,46	13040	141.0
(ex Seaforth Centurion-89)							
FAR CRUSADER (NIS)	1983	1989	68,00	15,88	6,47	13040	151.0
(ex Seaforth Crusader-89)							
FAR FOSNA (NOR)	1993	2766	74,90	18,00	6,01	14400	165.0
FAR GRIMSHADER (NIS)	1983	2528	80,85	17,52	5,00	12240	n/a
(ex Loch Grimshader-90; Far Scandia-89; Stad Scandia-89)							
FAR GRIP (NOR)	1993	2700	74,90	18,00	6,00	14400	165.0
FAR SAGA (NOR)	2001	3993	89,40	18,80	6,20	10656	n/a
FAR SAILOR (NIS)	1997	3057	74,90	18,00	6,60	16810	190.0
FAR SALTIRE (IOM)	2002	2000	73,60	16,80	6,10	16320	170.0
FAR SANTANA (NIS)	2000	3485	77,00	20,50	6,60	19230	180.0
FAR SCANDIA (NOR)	1991	2637	81,90	18,00	4,97	6600	n/a
FAR SCOTIA (IOM)	2001	1989	67,00	16,00	5,90	5378	n/a
FAR SCOUT (NOR)	2001	3100	80,00	18,00		16800	190.0

The FAR SCOUT is seen assisting the rig MAERSK JUTLANDER.

(Oyvind Halland)

FAR SENIOR (NIS)	1998	3125	80,60	18,00	6,60	16800	189.0
FAR SERVER (IOM)	1991	2610	81,90	18,00	4,97	6600	n/a
FAR SERVICE (IOM)	1995	3052	83,80	18,80	6,35	7200	n/a
FAR SLEIPNER (NIS)	1984	1910	67,48	16,82	6,08	10500	n/a
(ex Stad Sleipner-89)							
FAR SOUND	2006	3050	79,80	17,20	6,80	14400	150.0
FAR SOVEREIGN (NOR)	1999	4418	85,20	19,25	7,80	27400	280.0
FAR SPLENDOUR (NOR)	2003	2542	74,30	16,00	6,50	4350	n/a
FAR STAR (NOR)	1999	3104	84,00	18,80	6,20	9600	n/a
FAR STRAIT	2006	3050	79,80	17,20	6,80	14400	150.0
FAR STREAM	2006	3050	79,80	17,20	6,80	14400	150.0
FAR STRIDER (NOR)	1999	3009	82,85	19,00	6,33	6700	n/a
FAR SUPERIOR (IOM)	1990	2999	81,90	18,01	4,97	6600	n/a
FAR SUPPLIER (IOM)	1999	2989	82,85	19,00	6,33	6700	n/a
FAR SUPPORTER (IOM)	1996	2998	83,80	18,80	6,24	7200	n/a
FAR SWIFT (IOM)	2003	2149	71,90	16,00	6,00	5480	n/a
FAR SWORD	2006	3050	79,80	17,20	6,80	14400	150.0
FAR SYMPHONY (NOR)	2003	3585	86,20	19,00	6,65	5982	n/a
FAR VISCOUNT (IOM)	1982	1219	62,54	13,15	5,01	3410	n/a
(ex Seaforth Viscount-89)							
LADY MELINDA (NOR)	2003	2078	71,29	16,00	5,80	10750	65.0

The LADY ASTRID at Bergen in August 2003.

(Martin Penwright)

Managed by Farstad Shipping (India Pacific) Pty (Australia)

FAR SEA (NIS)	1991	2285	73,60	16,40	5,60	14400	150.0
FAR SKY (IOM)	1991	2285	73,60	16,40	5,60	14400	150.0
LADY ASTRID (NOR)	2003	2993	75,80	17,00	6,80	12070	152.5
LADY AUDREY (NIS)	1983	1979	67,74	15,62	6,43	12240	147.0
(ex Jarl Viking-94; Lowland Rambler-84; Atlantic Andwi-83)							
LADY CAROLINE (NOR)	2003	2993	75,80	17,20	6,80	12070	150.0
LADY CHRISTINE (NIS)	1985	2191	68,00	16,80	5,86	7200	n/a
(ex Shelf Supporter-01)							
LADY CYNTHIA (NIS)	1987	1997	69,16	15,00	6,09	9800	136.0
LADY DAWN (NIS)	1983	1768	69,15	15,00	6,24	12800	130.0
(ex Senorita-91)							
LADY ELIZABETH (NIS)	1983	1924	67,48	16,80	6,07	3500	n/a
(ex Maersk Assister-98; Mærsk Assister-95; Stad Neptun-87)							
LADY GERDA (NIS)	1987	1997	69,16	15,00	6,10	9800	136.0
(ex Shelf Ranger-01)							
LADY GRACE (IOM)	2002	1982	67,00	16,00	5,92	5378	n/a
LADY GRETE (NIS)	2002	2137	72,00	16,00		5378	n/a
LADY GURO (NIS)	2001	1706	61,90	15,50	5,75	5450	65.0
LADY KARI-ANN (NIS)	1982	1924	67,21	16,80	6,08	3478	n/a
(ex Maersk Attender-98; Mærsk Attender-95; British Amethyst-88; Sea Pearl-84)							
LADY MARGARET (NIS)	1993	1759	66,50	15,00	3,55		
(ex Shelf Challenger-01)							

| LADY SANDRA (NOR) | 1998 | 2598 | 73,75 | 15,40 | 6,90 | 16200 | 150.0 |
| LADY VALISIA (NIS) | 1983 | 1972 | 67,74 | 15,60 | 6,40 | 12240 | 142.0 |

(ex Far Supplier-95; King Supplier-87)
Offshore services in Europe, South America and Australasia

The NORTH CHALLENGER arrives in Aberdeen on the sunny evening of 7 July 2004.

(David Dodds)

GULFMARK NORGE AS

Strandgt. 5, 4307 Sandnes, Norway
Tel : +47 51 60 90 00   Fax : +47 51 60 90 01
E-mail : shipping@seatruck.no
Website : www.gulfmark.com
Livery - Dark blue hull, with white housing, wheelhouse and funnel with blue letter 'G'
NORTH

| CHALLENGER (NOR) | 1997 | 1968 | 67,02 | 16,00 | 5,91 | 5448 | n/a |
| NORTH CRUSADER (PAN) | 1984 | 1851 | 72,00 | 14,40 | 6,40 | 12000 | 140.0 |

(ex Stad Senja-89)

| NORTH FORTUNE (NOR) | 1983 | 2526 | 80,50 | 17,50 | 4,99 | 7120 | n/a |

(ex Skandi Fortune-01; North Fortune-90; Northern Fortune-89)

| NORTH MARINER (NOR) | 2002 | 3078 | 84,00 | 18,80 | 6,20 | 9600 | n/a |
| NORTH STREAM (NIS) | 1998 | 3106 | 84,40 | 18,80 | 6,25 | 9600 | n/a |

(ex Stream Truck-02)

| NORTH TRAVELLER (NOR) | 1998 | 1969 | 67,05 | 16,00 | 5,91 | 5448 | n/a |

(ex Stout Truck-02)

| NORTH TRUCK (NOR) | 1983 | 2597 | 80,77 | 18,00 | 4,98 | 6120 | n/a |

(ex Sound Truck-02)

NORTH VANGUARD (NOR)	1990	2637	81,90	18,00	4,97	6600	n/a
(ex Skandi Hawk-01)

| SENTINEL (GBR) | 1979/92 | 2652 | 81,26 | 18,30 | 4,32 | 4600 | n/a |

(ex Zacharias-04; Sea Truck-00; Nor Truck-88; Edda Sea-87; Flexservice 2-86)
Offshore services in the North Sea

J HAGENÆS SHIPPING AS

Tollbngt. 6, 6002 Ålesund, Norway
Tel : +47 70 12 40 78   Fax : +47 70 12 86 10
E-mail : mail@hagenaes.no

ACTIVE KING (GIB)	2005	2400	70,00			10800	

On bareboat charter to Seabulk Offshore Limited (USA)

| SEABULK ASIA (GIB) | 2003 | 2050 | 71,90 | 16,00 | 5,90 | 5370 | n/a |

(ex Active Princess-03)

HAVILA SUPPLY ASA

PO Box H, 6099 Fosnavåg, Norway
Tel : +47 70 08 09 00   Fax : +47 70 08 09 01
E-mail : office@havila.no
Website : www.havila.no
Livery - Green hull with white housing and wheelhouse

HAVILA (tbn)	2007		85,80	20,00			200.0
HAVILA (tbn)	2007		85,80	20,00			200.0
HAVILA CLEVER (GBR)	1975	1409	71,37	12,37	4,44	7040	150.0

(ex Kronbas-98; West Penguin-86; Atlantic Fosna-80; Edda Atlantic-76)

| HAVILA FAITH (IOM) | 1999 | 3017 | 82,85 | 19,02 | 6,35 | 6600 | n/a |

(ex Stirling Spey-05)

| HAVILA FAME (BHS) | 1995 | 2042 | 71,70 | 16,30 | 5,61 | 5440 | n/a |

(ex Smit-Lloyd Fame-05)

| HAVILA FAVOUR (IOM) | 1998 | 3017 | 82,85 | 19,02 | 6,35 | 6600 | n/a |

(ex Stirling Tay-05)

| HAVILA FORCE (IOM) | 2000 | 2528 | 73,80 | 16,29 | 6,50 | 15000 | 165.0 |

(ex Stirling Iona-05)

| HAVILA FORTRESS (BHS) | 1996 | 3017 | 82,88 | 19,29 | 6,32 | 4920 | n/a |

(ex Inverforth-05; Stirling Forth-02)

| HAVILA FORTUNE | 1992 | 2145 | 68,70 | 17,50 | 5,75 | 6610 | n/a |

(ex Stirling Pegasus-05; Star Pegasus-96)

| HAVILA HARMONY (NOR) | 2005 | 3996 | 92,95 | 19,70 | 6,30 | | |
| HAVILA RUNDE (NOR) | 1997 | 2017 | 69,00 | 16,00 | 6,00 | 7000 | n/a |

(ex Rescue Saga-98)

| HAVILA SEA (BHS) | 1975 | 1499 | 61,20 | 13,86 | 5,10 | 4200 | n/a |

(ex Emerald Bas-98; Emerald Sprite-92; Sprite-91; Edda Sprite-83)

| HAVILA SEARCHER (BHS) | 1975 | 1472 | 64,40 | 13,80 | 5,90 | 8000 | 105.0 |

(ex Rem Searcher-98; Plan Searcher-95; Pan Searcher-93; Far Searcher-90;
   Tender Searcher-87)

HAVILA SKY (GBR)	1957/85	579	56,74	9,35	4,50	2300	n/a
(ex Rescue Kim-98; Kim-95; Rescue Kim-92; Andenes-84; R 5-65)							
HAVILA STAR (BHS)	2000	1864	66,00	15,00	4,70	5434	n/a
HAVILA SUN (BHS)	1972	1151	58,40	11,70	4,35	2850	n/a
(ex Sunbas-98; Sun Tender-95; North Breeze-91; Ocean Range-90; Rembertiturm-88)							
HAVILA TERN (NOR)	1976	1104	58,72	11,52	4,20	1860	n/a
(ex Rescue Tern-98; West Tern-85)							
HAVILA TIGRIS (BHS)	2001	1864	66,00	15,00	4,70	5434	n/a
HAVILA TROLL (NOR)	2003	4537	92,40	18,00	5,20	14412	100.0

Offshore services worldwide

The HAVILA TERN leaves Aberdeen on 2 July 2004.

(David Dodds)

ISLAND OFFSHORE MANAGEMENT AS

Stalhaugen 5, 6065 Ulsteinvik, Norway
Tel : +47 70 00 97 50   Fax : +47 70 00 97 51

ISLAND (tbn)	2007		85,00	22,00			235.0
ISLAND CHAMPION	2006		93,00	20,00			
ISLAND FRONTIER (NIS)	2003	6834	106,20	21,00	6,30	14000	n/a
ISLAND PATRIOT	2005	3747	86,20	19,00	6,65	5982	n/a
ISLAND PIONEER	2006	5200	95,00	20,50	7,00	6800	
ISLAND PRIDE	2005	2265	71,90	16,00	6,00	5460	n/a
ISLAND RANGER	2005	3996	90,70	18,80	6,20	6800	n/a
ISLAND SCOUT (NIS)	2005	2152	71,90	16,00	6,00	5460	n/a
ISLAND SPIRIT	2005	2265	71,90	16,00	6,00	5460	n/a
ISLAND TRADER	2005	2265	71,90	16,00	6,00	5460	n/a
ISLAND VANGUARD	2006		85,00	22,00			235.0

Offshore services in the North Sea

The helicopter pad of the ISLAND FRONTIER is very prominent in this view of the vessel as she arrives at Aberdeen on 15 August 2004.

(David Dodds)

MAERSK SUPPLY SERVICE

50 Esplanaden, DK-1098, Copenhagen K, Denmark
Tel : +45 33 63 32 32   Fax : +45 33 6332 30
E-mail : cphsupplymng@maersk.com
Website : www.maersksupplyservice.com
Livery - Sky blue hull with cream housing

MAERSK								
ADVANCER	(IOM)	2004	6536	90,30	23,00	7,80	23500	280.0
MAERSK								
ASSERTER	(IOM)	2004	6536	90,30	23,00	7,80	23500	280.0
MAERSK BEATER	(IOM)	1997	4393	82,20	19,80	7,50	20020	237.0
MAERSK								
BONAVISTA	(CAN)	1983	2759	71,50	16,00	6,25	10800	125.0
(ex Bonavista Bay-87)								
MAERSK								
CHALLENGER	(CAN)	1986	2887	76,40	17,60	6,40	14400	192.0
(ex Oil Challenger-91; Challenger III-86; Sydfonn-86)								
MAERSK								
CHANCELLOR	(CAN)	1986	2887	76,40	17,60	6,40	14400	174.0
(ex Oil Chancellor-91; Kongshav-86)								
MAERSK								
CHIGNECTO	(CAN)	1983	2259	71,50	16,00	6,25	10800	142.0
(ex Chignecto Bay-87)								
MAERSK CUTTER	(GBR)	1983	1972	68,84	15,55	6,40	14400	182.0

MAERSK DEE (IOM)	2000	1863	56,64	14,60	6,02	6520	95.0
MAERSK DETECTOR (CAN)	2006		89,30	20,80		18280	212.0
MAERSK DISPATCHER (CAN)	2005		89,30	20,80		18280	212.0
MAERSK DON (IOM)	2000	1863	56,64	14,60	6,01	6520	95.0
MAERSK FINDER IOM)	1994	2961	82,50	18,85	6,25	7206	
MAERSK GABARUS (CAN)	1983	2259	71,50	16,00	6,25	10800	141.0
(ex Gabarus Bay-87)							
MAERSK HANDLER (IOM)	2002	3427	80,00	18,00	6,59	17500	198.0
MAERSK HELPER (IOM)	2002	3427	80,00	18,00	6,59	17500	198.0
MAERSK MAHONE (IOM)	1983	2259	71,50	16,00	6,25	10800	120.0
(ex Maersk Handler-02; Maersk Supporter-98; Mahone Bay-87)							
MAERSK MARINER (GBR)	1986	3949	82,00	18,40	6,90	14900	170.0
MAERSK PLACENTIA (CAN)	1983	2259	71,50	16,00	6,25	10800	142.0
(ex Maersk Shipper-97; Maersk Placentia-90; Placentia Bay-87)							
MAERSK RETRIEVER (GBR)	1979	1894	67,11	15,50	6,46	13000	152.0
MAERSK RIDER (GBR)	1982	1894	67,00	15,50	6,46	14400	181.0
MAERSK ROVER (GBR)	1982	1894	67,00	15,50	6,46	14400	161.0
MAERSK SEARCHER (IOM)	1999	4013	72,00	18,80	7,50	18250	200.0
MAERSK SERVER (IOM)	2000	4013	72,00	18,80	7,50	18250	200.0
MAERSK SHIPPER (IOM)	1999	4013	72,00	18,80	7,50	18250	200.0
MAERSK SUPPORTER (IOM)	1999	4013	72,00	18,80	7,50	18250	214.0

Two photographs of the Douglas-registered MAERSK SUPPORTER arriving in the New Waterway on 27 October 2003. She was towing the rig STENA DEE.

(Dominic McCall)

MÆRSK ACHIEVER (DIS)	2003	6536	90,30	23,00	7,80	23480	282.0
MÆRSK ASSISTER (DIS)	2000	6536	90,30	23,00	7,80	23480	282.0
MÆRSK ATTENDER (DIS)	2000	6536	90,30	23,00	7,80	23480	282.0
MÆRSK BATTLER (DIS)	1997	4393	82,20	19,80	7,50	20020	237.0
MÆRSK BLAZER (DIS)	1998	4393	82,20	19,80	7,50	20020	230.0

The MÆRSK BLAZER approaches Peterhead from the North Sea.

(The late Keith Morgan)

MÆRSK BOULDER (DIS)	1998	4393	82,20	19,80	7,50	20020	246.0
MÆRSK CHAMPION (DIS)	1986	2887	76,41	17,60	6,40	14400	177.0
(ex Oil Champion-92; Kongsgaard-87)							
MÆRSK CHIEFTAIN (DIS)	1985	2887	76,41	17,60	6,40	14400	177.0
(ex Oil Chieftain-92; Storfonn-87)							
MÆRSK CLIPPER (DIS)	1983	1972	68,84	15,55	6,40	14400	180.0
MÆRSK FEEDER (DIS)	1993	2961	82,50	18,80	6,24	7200	n/a
MÆRSK FETCHER (DIS)	1995	2961	82,50	18,80	6,24	7200	n/a
MÆRSK FIGHTER (DIS)	1992	2961	82,50	18,80	6,24	7200	n/a
MÆRSK FORWARDER (DIS)	1999	2961	82,50	18,80	6,24	7200	n/a
MÆRSK FRONTIER (DIS)	1992	2961	82,50	18,80	6,24	7200	n/a
MÆRSK LAUNCHER (DIS)	1988	2311	69,90	15,90	6,50	12000	152.0
MÆRSK LEADER (DIS)	1987	2311	69,90	15,90	6,50	12000	150.0
MÆRSK LIFTER (DIS)	1988	2311	69,90	15,90	6,50	12000	151.0
MÆRSK MASTER (DIS)	1986	3949	82,00	18,40	6,90	14900	170.0
MÆRSK PACER (DIS)	1991	2573	73,60	16,40	6,85	15600	187.0

MÆRSK

PROMOTER (DIS)	1992	2966	76,00	17,20	7,21	15600	198.5
MÆRSK PROVIDER (DIS)	1991	2473	73,60	16,40	6,85	15600	188.0
MÆRSK PUNCHER (DIS)	1992	2966	76,00	17,20	7,21	15600	198.5
MÆRSK SEEKER (DIS)	1999	4013	72,00	18,80	7,50	18250	200.0
MÆRSK SUPPLIER (DIS)	1999	4140	72,00	18,80	7,50	18250	200.0
MÆRSK TACKLER (DIS)	1983	1790	68,50	14,50	5,90	12240	129.0
(ex Tawaki-90; Federal Atlantic-86; Seaforth Atlantic-86)							
MÆRSK TERRIER (DIS)	1983	1621	67,70	14,50	5,95	12240	151.0
(ex Takapu-90)							
MÆRSK TOPPER (DIS)	1983	1621	67,70	14,50	5,95	12240	124.0
(ex Toanui-90)							
MÆRSK WINNER (DIS)	2003	6550	90,30	23,00	7,80	23480	278.0

Offshore services worldwide

The stern view serves to emphasise the size of the deck crane of the MÆRSK WINNER as she arrives in the River Scheldt.

(Martin Penwright)

O H MELING & CO A/S

Paradisveien 28, 4012 Stavanger, Norway
Tel : +47 51 50 55 60   Fax : +47 51 52 26 61
E-mail : ohmeling@ohmeling.no
Livery - Orange hull, buff housing and wheelhouse with orange band round top

SIDDIS MARINER	2006	3350	85,65	19,70			
SIDDIS PILOT (NOR)	1976	1125	58,25	12,02	4,12	6160	75.0
SIDDIS SAILOR (NOR)	1975	1324	68,80	12,00	4,12	3100	30.0
SIDDIS SKIPPER (NOR)	2003	2604	73,40	16,60	6,50	5520	n/a

Offshore services in the Norwegian sector of the North Sea

The SIDDIS SKIPPER was photographed off Stavanger.

(Oyvind Halland)

MYKLEBUSTHAUG MANAGEMENT AS

Fonnes Kai, 5953 Fonnes, Norway
Tel : +47 56 16 82 20   Fax : +47 56 16 82 21
E-mail : chartering@mmred.no
Website : www.mmred.no
Managed by Gulfmark Norge AS (Norway)

AQUARIUS (IOM)	1991	2650	81,90	18,00	4,97	6600	n/a
(ex Stirling Aquarius-04; Star Aquarius-96; Gerd Viking-94)							
MYKLEBUSTHAUG (tbn)	2005		73,60	16,00	5,90		

Offshore services in the North Sea

SIMON MØKSTER SHIPPING AS

Skogstostraen 37, 4029 Stavanger, Norway
Tel : +47 51 83 90 00   Fax : +47 51 83 90 90
E-mail : post@mokster.no
Website : www.mokster.no
Livery - Blue hull, white housing and wheelhouse; yellow funnel with company logo

STRIL CLIPPER (NOR)	1971	988	62,55	10,21	3,45	1155	32.0
(ex Donn Hugin-92; Tond-84; Bukkeskjell-82)							
STRIL MYSTER (NOR)	2003	3524	90,20	19,00	6,90	12745	n/a
STRIL NEPTUN (NOR)	1999	2423	70,40	16,00	6,80	7216	112.0

Vessel		Year	GT	Length	Beam	Draft	Power	Speed
STRIL ODIN		2006	3350	85,65	19,70			n/a
STRIL PIONEER	(NOR)	2003	5073	94,90	20,40	7,50	8157	n/a
STRIL POSEIDON	(NOR)	2003	4785	90,45	18,25	5,50	11560	n/a
STRIL POWER	(NOR)	1997	2926	74,90	18,00	8,00	14800	145.0
STRIL SAFETY	(NOR)	1949	834	58,76	9,02	6,35	1050	n/a

(ex Born Safety-87; Klara Birting-82; Knut Gronnevet-71; Gos 1-65; Knekt-55)

| STRIL SUPPLIER | (NOR) | 1999 | 3200 | 83,70 | 19,70 | 6,10 | 9036 | n/a |
| STRIL SUPPORTER | (NOR) | 1964 | 466 | 44,40 | 7,32 | 3,66 | 1942 | n/a |

(ex Striltral-90; Loranso-90; Anso-84; Torrand-82; Ingar Iversen-78; Ronstad-71;
Rembakk-67)

| STRIL SURVEYOR | (NOR) | 1936/90 | 644 | 55,88 | 8,12 | 6,26 | 1200 | n/a |

(ex Sartor-02; North-Sea Surveyor-90; Seaway Petrel-85; Vimi-82; Wih. Michaelsen-57)

| STRIL TENDER | (NOR) | 1965 | 541 | 47,17 | 8,40 | 4,44 | 1200 | n/a |

(ex Donn Myre-86; Myre Seadiver-85; Menes-83; Roeggen-80)

| STRILBORG | (NOR) | 1998 | 2955 | 74,90 | 18,00 | 8,00 | 14800 | 145.0 |
| STRILBRIS | (NOR) | 1947/77 | 430 | 46,85 | 7,50 | 3,67 | 880 | n/a |

(ex Sar Castor-02; Castor Tide-98; Hornbeck Castor-96; Seaboard Castor-95; Sartor-90;
Suet-67; Margat-59)

| STRILFALK | (NOR) | 1937/93 | 482 | 48,00 | 8,03 | 4,44 | 1100 | n/a |

(ex Sar Delta-02; Grampian Osprey-93; Sar Delta-93; Blue Safe-88; Lem Senior-81;
Polarbris I-66; Rau III-48)

| STRILFISK | (NOR) | 1960/85 | 343 | 41,86 | 8,41 | 3,70 | 495 | n/a |

(ex Grip-83)

| STRILHAUK | (NOR) | 1959/90 | 344 | 41,87 | 8,41 | 3,20 | 1320 | n/a |

(ex Sklinna-87)

| STRILHAV | (NOR) | 1963/82 | 750 | 56,59 | 9,00 | 4,03 | 1000 | n/a |

(ex Trønderhav-87; Volstad Senior-76)

| STRILHVAL | (NOR) | 1950/84 | 588 | 50,98 | 9,05 | 4,57 | 1600 | 30.0 |

(ex Kvintess-83; Kvint-78; Southern Jester-66; Kjapp-52; Kvint-51)

| STRILMØY | (NOR) | 2005 | 3380 | 85,65 | 19,70 | | | n/a |
| STRILODD | (NOR) | 1941/81 | 487 | 48,56 | 7,85 | 5,40 | 1040 | n/a |

(ex Tonjer-87; Bakk-81; Ole Bakk-79; Kos 39-62; Polarnacht-47)

| STRILVAKT | (NOR) | 1982 | 570 | 49,80 | 8,60 | 4,35 | 1500 | 25.0 |
| STRILVARD | (NOR) | 1952/82 | 843 | 63,50 | 9,05 | 5,58 | 1500 | n/a |

(ex Polarson-89; Torson-82; Meløyvær-76; Thorvard-67)

| STRILØY | (NOR) | 1930/72 | 466 | 46,57 | 7,28 | 4,22 | 990 | n/a |

(ex Geo Boy-89; Idol-77; Suderøy V-72; Hellesund-59; Suderøy-55)

Offshore supply and support services in the Norwegian sector of North Sea

OFFSHORE SUPPLY KS

P.O. Box 120, N-1325 Lysaker, Norway

| BREMONA | (BHS) | 2004 | 1643 | 63,40 | 15,00 | 4,90 | 7044 | 85.0 |

Offshore services

Late news : this vessel has been sold to owners outside Europe.

OLYMPIC SHIPPING AS

P.O. Box 234, 6099 Fosnavåg, Norway
Tel : +47 70 08 12 00   Fax : +47 70 08 12 01
E-mail : post@olympic.no
Website : www.olympic.no
Livery - Grey hull with white trim, white housing & wheelhouse; grey funnel with company logo

Name	Year						
OLYMPIC (tbn)	2006		79,80	17,20	6,80		200.0
OLYMPIC (tbn)	2006	2592	74,30	16,40	6,20	4024	
OLYMPIC COMMANDER (NIS)	2006	4641	93,00	19,70			n/a
OLYMPIC HERCULES (NOR)	2002	4325	82,10	20,00	7,50	23500	270.0
OLYMPIC ORION (NOR)	2002	3865	91,05	19,70	6,00	12925	n/a
OLYMPIC PEGASUS (NOR)	2002	4325	82,10	20,00	7,50	23500	270.0
OLYMPIC POSEIDON (NOR)	1998	3153	79,80	18,00	6,60	14400	175.0
(ex Stril Poseidon-98)							
OLYMPIC PRINCESS (NOR)	1999	3295	83,70	19,70		10332	n/a
OLYMPIC PROMOTER	2005	2165	73,60	16,00	5,90	5378	
OLYMPIC SUPPLIER (NOR)	1984	1987	67,83	15,60	6,46	13335	145.0
(ex Barra Supplier-95)							

Managed for Master Supply HS (Norway)

Name	Year						
OLYMPIC PROGRESS	2005	2165	73,60	16,00	5,90	5378	
OLYMPIC PROVIDER (NOR)	2004	2150	72,00	16,00	5,90	5460	n/a

Offshore services worldwide

The OLYMPIC PROVIDER passes Gorleston on her way into Great Yarmouth.

(Paul Gowen)

REMØY SHIPPING A/S

P.O. Box 53, 6099 Fosnavåg, Norway
Tel : +47 70 08 04 40   Fax : +47 70 08 93 37
E-mail : remoy.shipping@remoy.no

Livery - Red or blue hull with white housing and wheelhouse

REM STADT (NOR)	1995	3603	87,78	18,80	6,80	8800	n/a
REM SUPPLIER (NOR)	2005	2265	73,60	16,00	5,90	5378	
Managed for Nordsjøbas AS (Norway)							
HARSTAD (NOR)	2005	3132	83,00	15,50	6,00	10728	100.0
Managed for Kystvakten (Norway)							
ÅLESUND (NOR)	1996	1357	63,00	11,50		3600	50.0
Managed for REM Offshore (Norway)							
REM (tbn)	2006		92,95	19,70	6,30	5984	n/a
REM (tbn)	2007		92,95	19,70	6,30	5984	n/a
REM COMMANDER	2006		92,95	19,70	6,30	5984	n/a
REM FORTUNE	2006	3350	85,65	19,70			
Managed for Remship AS (Norway)							
GECO SCORPIO (NOR)	2000	1429	55,80	13,00		4774	45.0

Offshore services in the North Sea

The OCEAN COMMANDER of Rovde Shipping was photographed as she departed from Aberdeen on 11 December 2004.

(David Dodds)

ROVDE SHIPPING AS

6141 Rovde, Norway
Tel : +47 70 02 39 00   Fax : +47 70 02 26 52
E-mail : oddvar.strand@rovde.no
Website : www.rovde.no
Livery - Red hull with cream or white housing and wheelhouse

OCEAN CARRIER (BHS)	1996	3017	83,00	19,30	6,35	4920	n/a
(ex Inverclyde-05; Stirling Clyde-02)							
OCEAN COMMANDER (NOR)	1999	3465	84,30	18,80	6,20	9600	n/a
OCEAN FLOWER (NOR)	1974	1274	61,50	11,50	3,43	2000	n/a
(ex Normand Flower-85)							
OCEAN KNARR (NOR)	1985	1780	67,65	14,57	5,20	8640	
(ex Sun Supporter-92; Brodospas 42-91)							
OCEAN STAR (NOR)	1975	1513	69,85	12,50	5,91	3100	n/a
(ex Norindo Sun-85)							
SØLVBAS (NOR)	1974	1310	62,15	11,49	4,24	2000	n/a
(ex Normand Produce-85)							

Offshore services in the North Sea; also operate cable layers

SARTOR SHIPPING AS

5379 Steinsland, Norway
Tel : +47 56 31 94 00   Fax : +47 56 33 86 70
E-mail : shipping@sartor.no
Website : www.sartor.no
Livery - Red hull, white housing and wheelhouse

Managed for Ocean Alfa AS

SARTOR (NOR)	1976	2019	67,80	17,33	4,62	4200	n/a
(ex Northern Viking-04; Veronica Viking-97; Sealion Columbia-90; Active Duke-84)							

Managed for Ocean Mainport Ltd (Ireland)

OCEAN MAINPORT (NOR)	1976	2518	81,08	18,04	4,97	4800	n/a
(ex Olympic Commander-05; Northern Commander-96; Tender Commander-82)							
OCEAN SPIRIT (NOR)	1983	2169	69,09	17,51	5,02	6120	
(ex Far Spirit-05; Loch Shuna-89; Far Spirit-87; Stad Spirit-86)							

Managed for Team Atlantic AS

OCEAN FIGHTER (NOR)	1980	891	61,24	11,84	4,01	3200	n/a
(ex Stirling Tern-97)							
OCEAN SAFE (NOR)	1973	1154	58,33	12,63	5,27	5300	70.0
(ex Stril Odin-02; Odin Safe-96; Navimer II-90; Mærsk Tackler-89)							
OCEAN SKY (NOR)	1975	1314	64,55	13,83	3,23	7040	99.0
(ex Pan Sky-95; Far Sky-90; Stad Sky-86)							
OCEAN VIKING (NOR)	1986	2090	69,30	15,50	5,71	6000	n/a
(ex Viking Fighter-05; Tender Fighter-91)							
SIGGBAS (NOR)	1974	1104	58,72	11,52	3,81	2100	n/a
(ex West Plover-85)							
VIKING PRINCE (NOR)	1976	1322	64,54	13,83	4,72	7040	99.0
(ex Stad Supplier-89)							

Offshore services in the Norwegian sector of North Sea

The VIKING FIGHTER is seen near the Norwegian port of Stavanger. As we go to press, we learn that this vessel has been renamed OCEAN VIKING.

(Martin Penwright)

The SIGGBAS leaves Great Yarmouth on 24 September 2005.

(Bernard McCall)

SEANOR SHIPPING AS

P.O.Box 1514 Kjelvene, N-4093 Stavanger, Norway
Tel : +47 51 81 26 90   Fax : +47 51 91 26 91
E-mail : heross@online.no
Website : www.echoshipping.com

SILVER STAR	(PAN)	1973	1167	58,27	12,78	5,10	4200	n/a

   (ex Echo Star-05; Moresby-02; Echo Star-02; Malbun-02; Joyce Tide-89; Lady Joyce-74)
Offshore services in West Africa

SIEM OFFSHORE AS

P.O.Box 425, N-4664 Kristiansund S, Norway
Tel : +47 38 14 30 00   Fax : +47 38 14 30 01
E-mail : siemoffshore@siemoffshore.com
Website : www.siemoffshore.com
Livery - Blue hull with white housing and funnel

(tbn)	2006	2602	73,40	16,60	6,40	n/a
(tbn)	2006	2602	73,40	16,60	6,40	n/a
(tbn)	2006	2602	73,40	16,60	6,40	n/a
(tbn)	2006	2602	73,40	16,60	6,40	n/a
SASHA	2005	2602	73,40	16,60	6,40	n/a
SOFIE	2005	2602	73,40	16,60	6,40	n/a

Offshore services worldwide

SOLSTAD SHIPPING AS

P.O. Box 130, 4297 Skudeneshavn, Norway
Tel : +47 52 85 65 00   Fax : +47 52 85 65 01
E-mail : firmapost@solstad.no
Website : www.solstad.no
Livery - Orange hull, white housing & wheelhouse; buff funnel with company badge

NORMAND (tbn)		2007		81,00	20,00		20000	250.0
NORMAND ATLANTIC	(NOR)	1997	3663	80,40	18,00	7,77	20000	220.0
NORMAND AURORA		2005	3745	86,20	19,00	6,65	5982	n/a
NORMAND CARRIER	(NOR)	1996	3051	84,38	18,80	6,25	9100	n/a
NORMAND CUTTER	(IOM)	2001	10979	127,50	27,00	8,40	21800	n/a
NORMAND DRAUPNE	(NOR)	1985	3385	83,52	18,00	5,55	17932	175.0
NORMAND DROTT	(NOR)	1984	2686	75,50	16,60	5,61	12000	148.0
NORMAND FLIPPER	(NOR)	2003	3396	84,00	18,80	6,20	10196	n/a
NORMAND HUNTER	(MHL)	1982	1367	65,80	13,50	5,11	9800	120.0

   (ex A. H. Camogli-96; Edda Star-86)

NORMAND IVAN	(NOR)	2001	4604	81,00	20,00	7,61	20000	220.0

On 30 August 2004, the NORMAND IVAN was photographed alongside a barge laden with rig equipment at Stavanger.

(Martin Penwright)

NORMAND JARL (NOR)	1984	2686	75,50	16,60	5,60	12000	148.0
NORMAND MJOLNE (NOR)	1985	3385	83,45	18,00	5,57	17932	175.0
NORMAND NEPTUN (NIS)	1996	3663	80,40	18,00	7,77	20000	220.0
NORMAND PIONEER (IOM)	1999	5913	95,00	24,00	8,23	27800	286.0
NORMAND PRODUCE (NOR) (ex Troms Falken-05)	2001	2152	72,00	16,00	5,90	4010	n/a
NORMAND PROGRESS (IOM)	1999	5944	95,00	24,00	8,23	27800	304.0
NORMAND PROSPER (NIS)	1983	1636	75,65	13,82	4,71	9800	90.0
NORMAND RANGER (NOR)	1982	1338	64,85	13,81	4,72	8000	85.0
NORMAND SKARVEN (NOR) (ex Troms Skarven-05)	1986	3149	79,71	18,01	6,00	13200	150.0
NORMAND SKIPPER (NOR)	2005	4000	92,50	22,50		13000	n/a
NORMAND TITAN (NOR) (ex Troms Titan-05; Viking Titan-00; Polar Titan-91)	1985	2535	72,36	16,30	5,66	12600	140.0
NORMAND TRYM (NOR) (ex Randfonn-93)	1984	2019	67,85	15,60	6,43	12724	146.0

NORMAND VESTER (NOR) 1998		3061	84,38	18,80	6,25	9100	n/a

Managed for Solida KS (Norway)

NORMAND MARINER (NOR)	2002	4325	82,00	20,00	7,00	23500	270.0
NORMAND MASTER (NOR)	2003	4325	82,00	20,00	7,50	23500	270.0
NORMAND MERMAID (IOM)	2002	5528	90,10	20,50	7,00	14000	n/a

Managed for Island Offshore I KS (Norway)

NORMAND BORG (NIS)	2000	3140	80,00	18,00	6,00	16800	202.0

Managed for Island Offshore IV KS (Norway)

NORMAND FLOWER (NOR)	2002	5402	93,70	21,00	6,30	14000	n/a

Managed for Island Offshore III KS (Norway)

NORMAND ROVER (NIS)	2001	3835	92,40	18,80	6,21	10676	n/a

On bareboat charter to Seabulk Offshore Limited (USA)

SEABULK SOUTH ATLANTIC (NOR)	2003	2085	68,95	15,50	5,90	10800	105.0

(ex Troms Supporter-03)

Offshore services worldwide; also operates cable layers

With storm clouds as a backdrop and a distant rig virtually obliterated by mist and rain, the NORMAND BORG rides the swell in the North Sea and is highlighted by a rare shaft of sunlight on a day of changeable weather so often faced by the crews of supply vessels.

(James Dodds)

TAUBÅTKOMPANIET AS (operating as BOA OFFSHORE)

Pir II, 13A, Kai 9, N-7010 Trondheim, Norway
Tel : +47 73 99 11 99   Fax : +47 73 99 11 98
E-mail : office@boa.no
Website : www.boa.no
Livery - Red hull, white housing and wheelhouse; red funnel with company logo

BOA KING (BHS)	2001	2260	70,00	16,00	6,90	15150	200.0
Managed for Boa Deep C AS (Norway)							
BOA DEEP C (ESP)	2004	12473	119,30	27,00	8,80	25368	250.0
BOA DEEP C II (ESP)	2006	10000	119,30	27,00	8,80	27000	260.0
Managed for Boa Offshore AS (Norway)							
BOA QUEEN (BHS)	2001	2260	70,00	16,00	6,90	15150	200.0

Offshore services worldwide; also operates a fleet of tugs and barges

TRICO SUPPLY ASA

P.O. Box 85, 6099 Fosnavåg, Norway
Tel : +47 70 08 10 20   Fax : +47 70 08 93 2
E-mail : firmapost@tricosupply.no
Website : www.tricomarine.com
Livery - Red hull, cream housing; cream funnel with company logo

NORTHERN CANYON (BHS)	2002	3500	85,25	18,80		10662	n/a
NORTHERN CHALLENGER (NOR)	1992	2335	73,60	16,40	6,80	15612	170.0
(ex Brenda Viking-97)							
NORTHERN CHASER (GBR)	1991	2335	73,60	16,40	6,80	15612	166.0
(ex Andrew Viking-97)							
NORTHERN CLIPPER (NOR)	1994	2978	82,50	18,80	6,25	9600	n/a
NORTHERN COMMANDER (NOR)	1986	3149	79,71	18,01	6,00	13200	150.0
(ex Gullbas-97)							
NORTHERN COMRADE (NOR)	1985	1413	64,55	13,80	6,54	11140	145.0
(ex Arild Viking-97; King Supplier-89; Schelde-88; Balder Schelde-85)							
NORTHERN CORONA (NOR)	1991	2335	73,60	16,40	6,80	15612	170.0
(ex Ben Viking-97)							
NORTHERN GAMBLER (NOR)	1996	3041	84,00	18,80	6,23	7702	n/a
NORTHERN GENESIS (NOR)	1983	1899	67,30	16,80	6,08	3816	n/a
(ex Magnus Viking-97; Northern Clipper-89)							
NORTHERN MARINER (GBR)	1986	1532	60,20	14,40	5,70	3190	n/a
(ex Suffolk Mariner-97)							

Name (Flag)	Year						
NORTHERN PRINCESS (NOR)	1983	1242	58,53	13,00	4,72	4050	n/a
(ex Sira Odin-97; Sira Girl-83)							
NORTHERN QUEEN (GBR)	1982	1833	67,20	16,80	6,08	6880	n/a
(ex Mona Viking-97; Sea Guardian-90; Sea Worker-84)							
NORTHERN RIVER (NIS)	1998	3605	92,80	18,80	6,20	9600	n/a
NORTHERN SUPPORTER (GBR)	1996	1969	67,00	16,00	5,91	5448	n/a
(ex Suffolk Supporter-97)							
NORTHERN WAVE (NOR)	2002	3709	85,25	18,80	6,25	10662	n/a
On bareboat charter to Eidesvik AS (Norway)							
NORTHERN CRUSADER (NOR)	1992	2335	73,60	16,40	6,80	15612	178.0
(ex Monika Viking-97)							

Offshore services in the North Sea

The NORTHERN QUEEN arrives at IJmuiden on 4 August 2003.

(Dominic McCall)

TROMS OFFSHORE INVEST A/S

Strandveien 106, Lanes Center, N-9008 Tromsø, Norway
Tel : +47 77 67 99 50   Fax : +47 77 67 99 77
E-mail : offshore@tromsoffshore.no

TROMSFJORD	2005	2602	73,40	16,60	6,40

UGELSTADS REDERI A/S

Moloveien 3B, 6004 Ålesund, Norway
Tel : +47 70 10 26 60   Fax : +47 70 10 26 61
E-mail : post@ugelstad-rederi.no
Website : www.ugelstad.net
Livery - Dark orange, white housing and wheelhouse

ACTIVE GIRL (NOR)	1985	2562	80,77	18,00	4,96	5978	n/a
ACTIVE LORD (NOR)	1984	1823	65,20	15,50	4,98	6658	n/a
(ex Gro Viking-02; Lord Supplier-90)							
ACTIVE SWAN * (NOR)	2005	3000	93,40	19,20	6,60	5982	n/a
On bareboat charter to DOF Management AS (Norway)							
SKANDI WAVENEY (NIS)	2001	2164	71,90	16,00	5,90	4010	n/a

* ACTIVE SWAN currently on bareboat charter to Eidesvik as VIKING SWAN
Offshore services in the North Sea

The ACTIVE GIRL is seen underway off Stavanger.

(Oyvind Halland)

VIKING SUPPLY SHIPS AS

Markensgt 9, 4610 Kristiansand S, Norway
Tel : +47 38 12 41 70   Fax : +47 38 04 83 38
E-mail : vikingsupply@online.no
Website : www.vikingsupply.com
Livery - Black and yellow diagonal striped hull with yellow housing and wheelhouse
A. H. SAN

FRUTTUOSO (ITA)	2003	2725	74,20	16,90	6,95	15448	180.0

Managed for B & N Viking Icebreaking & Offshore AS (Sweden)

BALDER VIKING	(SWE)	2000	3382	83,70	18,00	7,20	18300	200.0
TOR VIKING II	(SWE)	2000	3382	83,70	18,00	7,20	18300	200.0
VIDAR VIKING	(SWE)	2001	3400	83,70	18,00	7,20	18300	200.0

Offshore services in the North Sea; also ice breaking duties in the Baltic

In the distinctive Viking livery of black and yellow, the BALDER VIKING approaches Aberdeen on 1 March 2004.

(David Dodds)

A rainbow attends the departure from Aberdeen of the VIDAR VIKING in May 2003.

(Martin Penwright)

VOLSTAD SHIPPING A/S

4 Klaus Nilsens Gate, Ålesund, Norway
Tel : +47 70 11 18 80   Fax : +47 70 11 18 81
Website : www.volstad.no

VOLSTAD (tbn)	2007	3000	93,40	19,20	6,80	9520	

ØSTENSJØ REDERI A/S

Smedasundet 97B, 5525 Haugesund, Norway
Tel : +47 52 70 45 45   Fax : +47 52 70 45 50
E-mail : post@ostensjo.no
Website : www.ostensjo.no
Livery - Orange hull, mustard housing & wheelhouse; white funnel with black stripe top and bottom with logo

EDDA (tbn)		2007		85,80	19,20	6,50	6798	
EDDA (tbn)		2007		108,70	23,00	7,80		
EDDA FJORD	(NOR)	2002	5886	98,16	22,00	8,50	14484	n/a
EDDA FONN	(NOR)	2003	4505	84,70	18,00	6,80	9656	n/a
EDDA FRAM	(NOR)	1987	2348	71,30	17,50	6,25	12240	n/a
EDDA FRENDE	(NOR)	1991	2775	87,10	17,50	6,20	6600	n/a
EDDA FREYA	(NOR)	1991	3000	87,10	17,50	6,20	6600	n/a
EDDA FRIGG	(NOR)	1997	2898	84,00	18,70	6,20	9566	n/a

Offshore services in the North Sea; also operates a fleet of tugs

With prominent helicopter platform, the EDDA FREYA arrives at Aberdeen on 26 September 2004.

(David Dodds)

AABENRAA PORT AUTHORITY
Mellemej 25, 6200 Aabenraa, Denmark
Tel : +45 7462 2514   Fax : +45 7462 3143
E-mail : port@aabenraakom.dk
Website : www.aabenraaport.dk

JULLE (DNK)	1980	17	11,50	4,30	1,70	400	4.0

Towage and pilotage services at Aabenraa

AALBORG HAVN
Langerak 19, P.O. Box 8530, 9220 Aalborg Øst, Denmark
Tel : +45 9930 1500   Fax : +45 9930 1515
E-mail : trafik@aalborghavn.dk
Website : www.aalborghavn.dk

ALBA (DNK)	1988	88	18,47	6,67	3,0	1019	14.0

Marine and towage services at Aalborg

PER AARSLEFF A/S
Lokesvej 15, DK-8230 Åbyhøj, Denmark
Tel : +45 8744 2222   Fax : +45 8744 2249
E-mail : info@aarsleff.com
Website : www.aarsleff.com

AARSLEFF X (DNK)	2002	28	14,62	5,02	2,12	345

Marine and civil engineering services around Denmark

ANDTRI TOWING ApS
Halsskovvej 91, DK-4420 Korsør, Denmark

VITUS (DIS)	1978	138	25,70	7,50	3,50	986	13.0

(ex Rauma IV-89; Wilhelm Hackman-84)
Towage services in Denmark and throughout Europe

BB TOWING & DIVING
Molevej 12, 6700 Esbjerg, Denmark
Tel : +45 7512 1350   Fax : +45 7513 3890
Website : www.towing-diving.dk

ALICE BEKKER (DIS)	1959	136	28,15	7,00	4,20	986	18.0
DIVER MASTER (HND)	1919	38	18,20	4,20	3,00	600	8.0

(ex Selene-94; Harta-91; Fairplay VII-91; Fairplay II-72)
(ex Voima; Rundik; Bill; Toy; Marcus; Stormqueen; Adolf; Monica; Lennart; Tyra; Halvard)
Towage and diving services around Denmark

BUGSERSELSKABET SKOVLAND

Møllevejen 76, 5960 Marstal, Denmark
Tel : +45 2344 6171

TENNESSE (DNK)	1959	39	18,40	4,99	2,66	790	10.0

(ex St. Serf-00; Mimer-92; Sct. Knud-88)
Towage services at Marstal but has latterly been lying at Fredericia

CASANI SØ-ENTREPRISE ApS

Jessens Mole 9A, 5700 Svendborg, Denmark
Tel : +45 6222 1121   Fax : +45 6221 7105
E-mail : casani@casani-saj.dk
Website : www.casani-saj.dk

RITA SAJ (DNK)	1938	94	24,34	6,18	2,60	675	

(ex Klumpen; Ramnes; Robbe)

SUSANNE SAJ (DNK)	1956	84	26,00	6,20	3,00	880	11.5

(ex Mester-05; Järven-70)

COPENHAGEN - MALMÖ PORT (CMP)

P.O. Box 2083, Ndr. Tolbod 7, DK-1013 Copenhagen K
Tel : + 45 33 47 99 99   Fax : +45 33 47 99 93
E-mail : cphport@cphport.dk
Website : www.cphport.dk

CAT-1 (DNK)	2004		12,52	4,96	1,20	279	2.4

Marine services in the port of Copenhagen

The ASTERIX at work in Fredericia on 16 June 2005.

(Bent Mikkelsen)

DANSK BJÆRGNING OG BUGSERING ApS

Nordre Kajgade 5, 9500 Hobro, Denmark
Tel : +45 9852 3727   Fax : +45 9852 4910
E-mail : dbb-salvage@post.tele.dk
Website : www.dbb-denmark.com

ASTERIX (DIS)	2003		32,22	11,70	5,27	5445	69.0
(ex Aeger-03)							
KATRINE (DIS)	2003	137	25,80	8,50	1,70	1950	24.5
(ex DMS Condor-02)							
LOUISE DIVER (DNK) *	1943	139	17,03		2,98	990	11.0
(ex Haahr Trumf-90; Jakob-87; ST. 252-52)							

Marine and civil engineering services around Denmark and elsewhere in Europe
* As this book goes to press, we learn that the LOUISE DIVER has been sold for the sum of 1 Euro to the Århus Maritime Historic Society and has reverted to the name JAKOB. She is to be a museum vessel in Århus.

DYKKERSELSKABET VIKING APS

Postbox 923, 3900 Nuuk, Greenland
Tel : +299 324828   Fax : +299 322948
E-mail : vikingcharter@greennet.gl

VIKING NAJA (DIS)	1963	218	29,40	8,30	3,90	1575	12.0
(ex Hargo-90; Karl-Erik-90; Hermes-84)							
VIKING POLAR (DNK)	1955	87	24,30	6,30	3,40	730	12.4
(ex Polardyk; Sveasund; Dorum)							

(NB - Suffered a broken crankshaft in summer 1998 and declared a constructive total loss; now awaits demolition)
Towage services at Nuuk in Greenland

ELSAM A/S

Overgade 45, 7000 Fredericia, Denmark
Tel : +45 7622 2000   Fax : +45 7622 1962
E-mail : info@elsam.dk
Website : www.elsam.com

CALORIUS (DIS)	1988	295	32,40	9,00	4,65	4590	60.0
JOULIUS (DIS)	1989	295	32,40	9,00	4,65	4590	60.0

ESBJERG HAVN

Auktionsgade 30, DK- 6700 Esbjerg, Denmark
Tel : +45 7512 9200   Fax : +45 7513 3167
E-mail : vagt@portesbjerg.dk
Website : www.portesbjerg.dk

ESBJERG 1 (DNK)	2002	176	22,50	7,25		2720	37.9

Towage and marine services around Denmark
Late news : This tug has been taken on bareboat charter by Svitzer Wijsmuller and renamed SVITZER APURE following transfer to Hamilton, Bermuda, her new port of registry.

FARVANDSVÆSENET

Overgaden oven Vandet 62 B, P.O. Box 1919, DK 1023 København K, Denmark
Tel : +45 3268 9500   Fax : +45 3257 4341
E-mail : frv@frv.dk
Website : www.fomfrv.dk

C.B. CLAUDI (DNK)	1979	57	20,00	6,42		1000	12.0

Maritime safety and rescue services around the Danish coast

FJORDUDVALGET FOR MARIAGER FJORD

9500 Hobro, Denmark.
Tel : +45 9851 1638

JACOB PETER (DNK)	1962	69	20,65	5,82	2,85	600	6.0

(ex Gorm-79)

Towage services on the Mariager Fjord

HALS UDDYBNING

Hals, Denmark

NIEREN (DNK)	1902/26/86	20	15,00	4,00	2,00	300	2.0

(ex Alfix; Veldig)
Based at Hals

The THOR was an unusual arrival at Kyle of Lochalsh in Spring 2005. She called to collect a barge for delivery to Greenland.

(Alistair MacDonald)

HANSTHOLM BUGSERSERVICE A/S

Kai Lindbergsgade 59, 7730 Hanstholm, Denmark
Tel : +45 9796 2999   Fax : +45 9796 2997
E-mail : nje@tugdk.dk
Website : www.tugdk.com

ODIN (DIS)	1981	142	26,30	7,40	3,80	1200	19.2
(ex Odin II-04; Goliath Thy-03; Tyr-96)							
THOR (DIS)	1998	84	20,88	6,00	3,10	1200	17.0

Towage services at Hanstholm; also worldwide towage

HIRTSHALS HAVN

Norgeskajen 11, Box 3, 9850 Hirtshals, Denmark
Tel : +45 9894 1422   Fax : +45 9894 4293
E-mail : havnevagtene@hirtshalshavn.dk
Website : www.hirtshalshavn.dk

HAVKATTEN III (DNK)	1986	23	12,95	4,00	2,90	596	7.0
(ex Ellen III-88)							
TYBRING (DNK)	1979	97	22,50	6,30	3,50	1300	13.0
(ex Kvarven-03; Oscar Tybring-86)							

Towage and marine services at Hirtshals

A new acquisition for the port of Hirtshals is the former Norwegian tug TYBRING. She is seen in her new home port on 30 August 2005.

(Bent Mikkelsen)

HUNDESTED HAVN
Amtsvejen 2, 3390 Hundested, Denmark
Tel : +45 4793 7234   Fax : +45 4793 7578
E-mail : hundested-havn@image.dk

BULLER (DNK)	1955	20	16,00	4,40	2,50	500	7.0

(ex Kurer Stevns-82; Kurer-71)

A fine view of the BULLER at Hundested on 17 August 2005.

(Bent Mikkelsen)

J. A. REDERIET
Brå Møllevej 11, 8781 Stenderup, Denmark
Tel : +45 7565 0094   Fax : +45 7565 0994
E-mail : j.alfastsen@image.dk
Website : www.jarederiet.com

LUNA A (DIS)	1976	358	34,50	9,40	3,51	2320	41.0

(ex Hermes-04; Bugsier 9-77)

SANNE A (DNK)	1908	33	18,50	4,20	2,30	343	5.0

(ex Else Wejse; Lillesund; Ingrid Tug; Goliath Fur; Alert)

SUSANNE A (DIS)	1977	277	32,92	9,61	4,17	2640	35.0

(ex Big-02; Sun Essex-00)
Coastal towage around Europe

JENS LARSEN SHIPPING
Havretoften 36, 5700 Svendborg, Denmark
Tel : +45 6222 0203   Fax : +45 6222 0253

ACTIV (DNK)	1955	15	16,00	4,52	1,75	230	3.0

(ex Alert-94; Anegen-91; Gerjo-59)

ACTIV 2 (DIS)	1967	52	17,10	5,70	2,50	475	8.0

(ex Eol-98; Holländeren-85)
Towage and marine services at Svendborg; also coastal towage around Europe

The three tugs of the Alfastsen (J A Rederiet) fleet were photographed on Horsens Fjord on 28 October 2004.

(Bent Mikkelsen)

KOLDING HAVN

Jens Holms Vej 1, 6000 Kolding, Denmark
Tel : +45 7550 2066   Fax : +45 7550 2058
E-mail : koldinghavn@kolding.dk
Website : www.koldinghavn.dk

CASPAR (DNK)	1989	13	12,00	4,00	1,70	493	7.0

Towage and icebreaking duties at the port of Kolding

KORSØR HAVNESMEDIE ApS

Amerikakaj 2, 4220 Korsør, Denmark
Tel : +45 5857 0085   Fax : +45 5857 1485

HELENE C (DNK)	1978	16	11,90	4,00	1,80	300	4.0

(ex Thor Stevns-92)
Towage services at Korsør

KØGE BOATMAN CO.

Carlsensvej 35, 4600 Køge, Denmark

FRANK (DNK)	1972	12	12,01	3,35	1,40	240	3.5

Towage and marine services at Køge

NAKSKOV HAVNEUDVALG

Havnegade 2, 4900 Naksov, Denmark
Tel : +45 5492 0313   Fax : +45 5492 5113
E-mail : havnen@naksov.dk

NAKSKOV HAVN II	(DNK)	1980	16	11,85	4,00	1,65	660	5.0
(ex Urd-97)								

Towage and marine services at Nakskov

With evidence of a storm not too far away, the STEVNS OCEAN passes Gorleston on her way out of Great Yarmouth.

(Paul Gowen)

NORDANE SHIPPING AS

Faergevej 5, DK-5700 Svendborg, Denmark
Tel : +45 6222 2777   Fax : +45 6222 2551
E-mail : info@nordane.dk
Website : www.nordane.dk
Livery - Green hull with white housing. Black funnel with white band and green 'S'

CAP STEVNS	(DNK)	1962	122	25,00	7,00	3,35	1585	18.0
(ex Eikvaag-86; Svava-83)								
ODIN STEVNS	(DNK)	1960	40	18,20	4,95	2,60	600	6.0
(ex Dagmar-90; Goliath-83)								
STEVNS	(DNK)	1975	163	27,50	7,50	3,50	2000	14.0
(ex Goliath Fur-01; Mimer-96; Weswear-94; Brage-89)								
STEVNS ARCTIC	(DIS)	2005	512	33,50	11,60	5,20	5027	65.0
STEVNS GUARD	(DNK)	1977	123	24,39	8,18	4,10	1860	18.5
(ex Grane-01; Grane III-92; Brage-91)								

STEVNS ICEBIRD (DIS)	1970	291	31,80	9,60	4,70	3700	40.0
(ex Rauni-00; Skuld-95)							
STEVNS MASTER (DIS)	1971	282	31,10	8,80	5,40	2000	30.0
(ex Lankenau-98)							
STEVNS OCEAN (DIS)	2003	512	33,50	11,60	5,20	5027	65.0
THOR STEVNS (DNK)	1951	99	25,60	6,58	3,10	1160	12.6
(ex Stevns Tug; Grane)							

Towage at various Danish ports; also coastal towage

PORT OF NYKØBING (FALSTER)
Havnepladsen 4, 4800 Nykøbing F, Denmark
Tel : +45 5485 0563   Fax : +45 5482 0564
E-mail : vis@nyk-f-kom.dk

RAS (DNK)	1956	19	15,50	4,20	1,80	550	4.0
(ex Helmer-02; Goliath V-80)							

Towage and marine services at Nykøbing (Falster)

NÆSTVED HAVN
Toldbodgade 4, 4700 Næstved, Denmark
Tel : +45 5578 5182   Fax : +45 5578 5183
E-mail : port@naestvedport.dk
Website : www.naestvedport.dk

ENØ (DNK)	1979	48	17,00	5,50	2,20	350	3.0

Towage services at Næstved

The ENØ is seen in her home port of Næstved in July 1993.

(Bernard McCall)

OHLSSON & LINDE SHIPPING A/S

12 Havnen, PO Box 10, DK-4600 Køge, Denmark
Tel : +45 5665 0006   Fax : +45 5665 2556
E-mail : mail@ols.dk

ROLLO (DNK)	1952	19	15,00	4,00	1,40	210	3.0

(ex Hop III-83; Attach 10-77)
Towage services at Faxe Ladeplads

LARS BERENTZ PEDERSEN

Nibe, Denmark

LIMFJORD (DNK)	1902	20	14,50	4,00	2,90	303	4.0

(ex Activ-94; Hop II-86; Stormcenter-73; Arne-66; Bill-51; Dux)
Based in the Limfjord for dredging support

PETERSEN & SØRENSEN

Svendborg, Denmark

MALOU (DNK)	1960	27	16,50	4,30	1,90	232	3.0

(ex Tit-03)
Based at the Marstal shipyard of her owners

RANDERS HAVNEVÆSEN

Kulholmsvej 1, 8900 Randers, Denmark
Tel : +45 8642 1057   Fax : +45 8640 7181
E-mail : randershavn@randers.dk

JENS OVE (DNK)	1981	60	19,50	5,80	2,95	900	7.0

Towage services at Randers

ROHDE NIELSEN A/S

Nyhavn 20, 1051 København, Denmark
Tel : +45 3391 2507   Fax : +45 33912514
E-mail : mail@rohde-nielsen.dk
Website : www.rohde-nielsen.dk

LOKE R (DIS)	1971	127	26,40	8,31	2,91	986	14.0
VIDAR R (DNK)	1980	20	15,25	4,75	2,00	525	5.0

(ex Darsser Ort-95) *(LOKE R)*
(ex Kildary) *(VIDAR R)*
Marine and civil engineering services around Denmark

RØNNE HAVNEVÆSEN

Munch Petersens Vej 2, 3700 Rønne, Denmark
Tel : +45 5695 0678   Fax : +45 5695 0631
E-mail : hvan@roennehavn.dk
Website : www.roennehavn.dk

URSUS (DNK)	1995	83	19,74	6,30	2,60	690	12.0

Towage services at Rønne

P/R SKAWLINK

Auktionsvej 10, P.O. Box 132 - 9990 Skagen, Denmark
Tel : +45 9844 3311   Fax : +45 9845 0029
skawlink@saga-shipping.dk
Website : www.saga-shipping.dk/skawlink

SOUNDLINK (DNK)	1975	30		4,20	2,30	320	5.0
(ex Skawlink-04; Lene-92; Salen II)							
SKAWLINK I (DNK)	1974	20	11,37	4,86	1,94	275	5.0
(ex Eft-04; Efta 3-90; Max-86)							
SKAWLINK III (DNK)	2003	78	20,40	6,60	3,20	700	9.0

Towage and marine services at Skagen; SOUNDLINK is based at Copenhagen

PETER SORENSEN

Vordingborg, Denmark

SONTINJA (DNK)	1968	75	20,71	6,60	3,00	600	7.0
(ex Tina A-04; Stevns; Bamble; Sterke; Nils)							

The SONTINJA at Esbjerg on 20 December 2004.

(Bent Mikkelsen)

PORT OF STRUER

Godthåbsvej 4-6, 7600 Struer, Denmark
Tel : +45 9785 0228   Fax : +45 9785 5434
E-mail : hs-havn@post4.tele.dk

BUTLER (DNK)	1976	16	12,00	4,00	2,00	270	3.0
(ex Juno-94)							

Towage and marine services at Struer

SVENDBORG BUGSER A/S

Nordre Kajgade 9A, 5700 Svendborg, Denmark
Tel : +45 6222 2911   Fax : +45 6222 2555
E-mail : info@svendborgbugser.dk
Website : www.svendborgbugser.dk

DANASUND (DIS)	1993	23	16,50	5,20	2,10	816	11.0
(ex Lillebælt-97)							
EUROSUND (DIS)	1979	406	35,00	9,80	4,70	3520	54.4
(ex Formidable-01)							
NORSUND (DIS)	1971	282	31,10	8,80	5,40	2000	30.0
(ex Ronnebeck-97)							
SKANSUND (DIS)	1982	36	15,70	4,90	2,10	730	11.0
(ex Albicore B-96)							
STORESUND (DIS)	1969	122	26,00	7,20	3,12	1100	18.5
(ex Stein-98)							
SVEASUND (DIS)	1969	138	26,00	7,60	3,65	1320	24.0
(ex Jade-93)							
WESTSUND (DIS)	1980	366	33,24	10,28	4,70	2820	38.0
(ex Strathfoyle-02; Clausentum-94)							

Coastal towage around Denmark and Europe

The fabrication of ship sections in yards in eastern Europe and subsequent completion in western Europe has become commonplace in the shipbuilding industry. The NORSUND passes through the Kiel Canal on 27 July 2005 towing a barge bearing the bridge section of a ship from Gdansk to the well-known shipyard of J J Sietas on the outskirts of Hamburg.

(Bent Mikkelsen)

EM. Z. SVITZER A/S

Pakhus 48, Sundkaj 9, 2100 København Ø, Denmark
Tel : +45 3919 3919   Fax : +45 3919 3909
E-mail : emz@svitzer.dk
Website : www.svitzerwijsmuller.com

Livery - Dark blue hull, cream housing & dark blue funnel with a blue 'maltese' cross

BAUGE	(BHS)	1981	235	29,50	8,50	4,25	2480	32.0
BESTLA	(DIS)	1981	235	29,50	8,50	4,25	2480	32.0

The BESTLA underway at speed.

(Jan Rautawaara)

BURE	(BHS)	1982	235	29,50	8,50	4,25	2480	32.0
EGIL	(DIS)	1987	376	33,10	10,00	4,27	4540	60.0
(ex Stevns Bugser-00; Maria Isabel I-98)								
FENJA	(DNK)	1999	453	33,60	10,20	5,25	4900	64.0
FRIGGA *	(DNK)	1998	453	33,60	10,20	5,25	4900	62.0
GARM	(DNK)	1974	17	12,60	4,30	2,20	700	7.5
(ex Goliath I-93)								
HUGIN	(DNK)	1980	61	19,50	6,52	3,60	1160	17.0
(ex Goliath Carl-99; Svava-93; Goliath Røn-83)								
MIMER **	(DNK)	1975	192	27,00	8,49	3,59	2320	30.0
(ex Stevns-01; Montenovo-98; Selat Harima-96; Navid-93; Al Alliah-92)								
SIGYN	(DIS)	1996	485	33,80	10,20	5,12	4000	51.0
SKULD	(DIS)	1996	485	33,80	10,20	5,12	4000	51.0
SLEIPNER ***	(DIS)	1981	352	33,50	9,50	4,25	3180	50.0
SVAVA	(DNK)	1977	50	18,50	5,60	2,60	1400	14.0
(ex Goliath Carl-93)								
SVITZER MARS	(DIS)	2004		33,30	11,50	4,80	4820	66.0

The SVITZER MENJA at Fredericia on 5 September 2005.

(Bent Mikkelsen)

SVITZER MENJA (DNK)	2005		33,30	11,50	4,80	4820	66.0
SVITZER MJØLNER (DIS)	2004		33,30	11,50	4,80	4820	66.0
SVITZER MUNIN (VCT)	1974	353	32,50	9,75	5,75	3900	38.0
(ex Dynan-04)							
URD (DNK)	1973	17	12,60	4,30	2,20	700	7.5
(ex Goliath IV-98)							
VALKYRIEN *** (DIS)	1983	291	31,85	9,00	4,85	3710	52.0
VØLUND *** (DIS)	1983	291	31,85	9,00	4,85	3710	50.0

* To be transferred to the Norwegian flag for the duration of a bareboat charter to Bukser and Berging and renamed BRYTEREN
** Stationed at Puerto Cabello, Venezuela, for the duration of a bareboat charter (with purchase option) to Zulia Towing
*** The pusher tugs SLEIPNER, VALKYRIEN and VØLUND have been sold to a UK-based Danish owner to be handed over on 31 December 2005
Towage services at various Danish ports
Part of the Svitzer-Wijsmuller group

SØNDERBORG HAVNEVÆSEN
Passagerkajen, 6400 Sønderborg, Denmark
Tel : +45 7442 2765   Fax : +45 7443 3019
E-mail : havnen@sonderborg.dk
Website : www.sonderborg.dk

BALDER (DNK)	1977	17	19,00	4,00	1,80	300	4.0
(ex Odin Stevns-85)							

Towage and ice-breaking duties at Sønderborg

VEJLE HAVNEVÆSEN

Parkhusgade 5, 7100 Vejle, Denmark
Tel : +45 7582 0466   Fax : +45 7583 8754
E-mail : vejle.havn@mail-telia.dk
Website : www.vejleport.dk

JEPPE JENSEN (DNK)	1965	50	15,40	5,50	3,00	280	4.1

Towage and pilotage services at Vejle

VLIELAND APS

P.O. Box 23, 5800 Nyborg, Denmark
Mobile tel : +45 20663353
E-mail : tug@vlieland.dk
Website-www.vlieland.dk

VLIELAND (DIS)	1970	69	22,50	6,80	3,60	1362	21.0

Coastal towage around Europe but stationed at Fort de France, Martinique, since 2003

ÅRHUS HAVN

Mindet 2, P.O. Box 130, 8100 Århus C, Denmark
Tel : +45 8613 3266   Fax : +45 8612 7662
E-mail : port@aarhus.dk
Website : www.aarhushavn.dk

AROS (DNK)	2003	450	28,67	10,43	4,65	4750	55.0
HERMES (DNK)	1978	269	31,50	10,10	4,60	4200	46.0

(ex Bremerhaven-86)
Towage services at Århus

The HERMES assists a bulk carrier at Århus on 18 May 2004. The AROS is visible at the stern.
(Bent Mikkelsen)

TUGS - ESTONIA

BALTIC SHIP REPAIRERS
Kopli tn. 103, 11711 Tallinn, Estonia
Tel : +372 6 102201   Fax : +372 6 102496

RUMB (EST)	1966	130	28,82	7,42	2,80	400
(ex MB 6130)						
VELA (EST)	1964	114	28,81	6,76	2,35	400
(ex Antey-93; MB 6099)						
VENE (EST)	1979	187	29,30	8,31	3,40	1200
(ex Baltiets)						

Towage services at Tallinn shipyard

BLRT GRUPP AS
Kopli tn. 103, 11712 Tallinn, Estonia
Tel : +372 6 102315   Fa x : +372 6 1029
E-mail : port@bsr.ee
Website : www.bsr.ee

TUGEV (EST)	1990	182	29,30	8,59	3,65	1604
(ex Russo Balt-93)						
AMIGO (EST)	1979	187	29,30	8,49	3,80	1200

Towage services at Tallinn

The ODIN I was photographed at Paljassaare on 12 June 2003.

(Barry Standerline)

EURO-BALTIC SHIPPING SERVICES LTD

PO Box 3717, 10508 Tallinn, Estonia
Tel : +372 6419150   Fax : +372 6419139
E-mail : shipping@ebss.ee
Website : www.ebss.ee

ODIN 1 (EST)	1975	196	29,16	7,95	3,75	2320	30.0
(ex Mjølner-03)							
ODIN III (EST)	1981	87	19,50	6,52	3,60	1160	17.0
(ex Goliath Gol-03)							
VEGA 1 (EST)	1992	182	29,00	8,24	3,40	1600	22.0
(ex Butegarth-03; E.L. Preston-02; Imakon-94)							

Towage work with the company's fleet of barges

ESTONIAN SHIP MANAGEMENT LTD

113A Kadaka Street, 0026 Tallinn, Estonia
Tel : +372 6 579901   Fax : +372 6 563686
Managed for Hoiupanga Liisingu AS

ARNO (EST)	1975	134	25,76	3,40	1160
(ex Rauma I-98)					

Towage services at Muuga Harbour, Tallinn

KUNDA NORDIC CEMENT CORP

Jaama Str.2, 44106 Kunda, Estonia
Tel : +372 322 9900   Fax : +372 1546
E-mail : knc@knc.ee
Website : www.knc.ee

KUNDA (SWE)	1968	243	30,03	8,67	4,20	2475
(ex Karlshamn-03)						

Towage services at Kunda

LOKSA SHIP REPAIR YARD

Tallinna mnt.2, 3020 Harjumaa, Estonia

KARIN (EST)	1969	112	23,50	7,42	2,70	600

Towage at Loksa Shipyard

MOONSUND SHIPPING

Ranna tn.26-7, 3300 Kuressaare, Estonia
Tel : +372 245 57178   Fax : +372 245 56700

UKU (EST)	1960	116	28,80	6,82	2,43	400
(ex Lielirbe; MB 6072)						

Towage services throughout Estonia

PÄRNU PORT AUTHORITY

Lootsi tn.6, 80012 Pärnu, Estonia

RUDOLF (EST)	1949	165	27,54	8,13	4,00	1500

(ex Amazon-00; Vølund-81; Rudolf-72)
Icebreaking and towage services at Parnu

PKL LTD

Lootsi 11, 10151 Tallinn, Estonia
Tel : +372 6 318151   Fax : +372 6 313100
E-mail : info@pkl.ee
Website : www.pkl.ee

ERIDAN (EST)	2004	468	31,49	12,10	3,89	5000	63.5
H. KANTER (EST)	2002	439	31,36	12,10	3,78	4340	55.0
MARS (EST)	2000	430	32,70	10,50	4,10	3590	45.0
ORION (EST)	1986	182	29,30	8,60	3,65	1580	20.0

The ORION is an example of a standard class of tugs built in Russia from the mid-1980s. She was photographed at Tallinn on 29 August 2000.

(Dominic McCall)

PRANGLI (EST)	1983	228	35,83	9,01	3,18	2486	30.0
SATURN (EST)	2004	144	19,00	9,00	3,80	2810	35.0
SIRIUS (EST)	1989	165	23,50	9,00	3,25	804	9.6
(ex Gerakl-99)							
SOMERI (EST)	1987	270	33,70	9,00	3,27	2486	30.0
(ex Symeri-92)							

TASUJA (EST) (ex Peresvet-92)	1988	182	29,30	8,24	3,65	1604	20.0
TOM T (EST) (ex Tom-95)	1991	182	29,30	8,60	3,65	1580	20.0
URAN (EST)	2004	144	19,00	9,00	3,80	2810	35.0

Towage services at Tallinn

Again seen at Tallinn on 29 August 2000, the SIRIUS is a multi-purpose tug. This stern view shows that she is equipped to work as a pusher tug.

(Dominic McCall)

VAGGEN AS

Tööstuse tn.46, 10416 Tallinn, Estonia
Tel : +372 646 4601   Fax : +372 646 4200

MONTU (EST) (ex Suur Tyil-92)	1972	187	29,30	1200

Towage services at Tallinn

VAVEKOR LTD (VAVEKOR AS)

Lume tn.14, 10416 Tallinn, Estonia

PEETER (EST)	1956	109	28,80	6,76	2,39	400

TUGS - FINLAND

AJOHINAUS PEKKA RYTKÖLÄ KY
Urheilijankatu 8, 48130 Kotka, Finland

AJO (FIN)	1959	29	17,46	4,10	2,10

ASIKAINEN MARKKU & KÖPMAN FRANS
Helsinki, Finland

ORJAKU (FIN)	1955	109	26,40	6,50	3,20	1588

A-SUKELLUS
Pansiontie 28, Turku, Finland

NEMO (FIN)	1953	24	13,15	3,99	1,80

(ex Ii 2; Stor-Hacke)

AUTERIEN JUKKA
Ahopellontie 21, 42100 Jämsä, Finland

VOITTO (FIN)	1877	68	22,90	4,80	2,15

(ex Houru)
Towage services in the Saimaa lakes

BOSKALIS NORDIC OY / TERRAMARE OY
Laurinmäenkuja 3 A, PB 14, FIN-00441, Finland
Tel : +358 9 613 621   Fax : +358 9 613 62700
E-mail : terramare@terramare.fi
Website : www.terramare.fi

HALLI (FIN)	1980	10	10,05	3,45	1,70		
SAMI (FIN)	1975	16	11,56	4,28			
SPARK (FIN)	1999					498	7.0
TERTTU (FIN)	1975	17	12,00	4,20	1,90	308	3.5

Marine civil engineering and dredger support

CONTAINERSHIPS LTD OY
Mannerheimintie 15 B, 00260 Helsinki, Finland
Tel : +368 9 615 311   Fax : +358 9 407 107
E-mail : sales@containerships.fi
Website : www.containerships.fi

LITKE (RUS)	1950	195	30,00	7,53	3,80	2169	25.0

(ex Emil-02; Puuma-93; Nalle-88; Porin Nalle-81; Porin Karhu-76)
Towage services at the Litke Bay Terminal in St. Petersburg, Russia

ESL SHIPPING

Suolakivenkatu 1 A, 00810 Helsinki
Tel : +358 9 759 5777   Fax : +358 9 787 315
Website : www.eslshipping.fi

ALFA (FIN)	1975/92	272	29,00	8,70	4,40	3450	38.0
(ex Hermes-01; Hepa-88; Urho-76)							
BRAVO (FIN)	1967	249	30,14	8,40	4,50	3400	33.0
(ex Mercurius-01; Dox-98; Ben-95; Baldur-89; Beni-79)							

Pusher services with company's fleet of barges in the Baltic Sea

FINNLINES PLC

P.O. Box 197, 00181 Helsinki, Finland
Tel : +358 10 34350   Fax : +358 10 3434425
E-mail : info@finnlines.fi
Website : www.finnlines.fi

Managed for Merita Rahoitus OY

RAUTARUUKKI (FIN)	1986	1562	41,70	15,50	6,70	10440	n/a
STEEL (FIN)	1987	1562	41,70	15,50	6,70	10440	n/a
(ex Finn-91)							

Pusher tugs handling barges around Finland and the Baltic

An increasingly common feature of the shipping scene in Scandinavia is the transportation of bulk cargoes such as coal or iron ore in huge barges. Timber is also transported in this way. The barges are pushed by powerful pusher tugs. Bearing the familiar Finnlines funnel colours, the tug STEEL is seen at Riga on 27 September 1993 as she pushes the appropriately-named barge BULK. It can be seen that the tug/barge combination has been constructed in such a way that the tug sits neatly inside the stern section of the barge.

(Jan Rautawaara)

FINTASHIP

Shipping Enterprise, Valimontie 16, 00380 Helsinki, Finland
Tel : +358 30 620 7000
E-mail : firstname.lastname@finstaship.fi
Website : www.fintaship.fi

APU (FIN)	1970	4121	86,50	21,30	7,20	13950	125.0
KONTIO (FIN)	1987	7066	98,60	24,20	8,00	29700	160.0
OTSO (FIN)	1986	7066	99,00	24,20	8,00	29700	160.0
SISU (FIN)	1976	7525	106,60	23,80	8,30	21730	185.0
URHU (FIN)	1975	7525	106,60	23,80	8,30	21730	185.0
VOIMA (FIN)	1970	4159	83,50	19,40	7,00	13680	113.0

Icebreaking services in the Baltic
Part of the Finnish Maritime Administration

FORTUM OIL & GAS OY

Keilaniemi, 00048 Espoo, Finland
Tel : +358 10 4511   Fax : +358 10 452 4798
E-mail : shipping@fortum.com
Website : www.fortumshipping.com

AHTI (FIN)	2002	560	33,50	12,80	6,30	6350	70.0
AULIS (FIN)	1981	263	30,00	10,00	4,20	3200	40.0
ESKO (FIN)	1981	263	30,00	10,00	4,20	3200	40.0
KARI (FIN)	1981	263	30,00	10,00	4,20	3200	40.0
UKKO (FIN)	2002	560	33,50	12,80	6,30	6350	70.0

Towage and ice-breaking services at Fortum's oil terminals & handling the company's barges

FURU MAURI

Kiertotie 9, 71800 Siilinjärvi, Finland

TOLVAN (FIN)	1944	86	22,70	6,08	2,90	

(ex No. 12 - 48, ST 480 - 46)
Towage services in the Saimaa lakes

REINO HENRIKSSON OY

Wredentie 9, 07900 Loviisa, Finland
Tel : +358 19509111   Fax : +358 19535800
E-mail : reino.henriksson@kolumbus.fi

Managed for Henric Tow Oy (Finland)

HENRIC (FIN)	1969	347	36,56	10,01	3,96	3380	50.0

(ex Njord-03; Nord-01; Njord-01; Henric-98; Brackengarth-95)
Coastal towage around the Baltic Sea

HH HINAUS OY A/B

Varpuspolku 12, 07920 Loviisa, Finland
Tel : +358 19 515678

AASLA (FIN)	1925	148	24,88	7,33	2,86	1385	
(ex Risto-99; West-97; Hermes af Stockholm-93; Tornen-89; Bulbider-88; Hermes-86)							
HIRN (FIN)	1958	149	26,01	7,80	3,53	1243	
(ex Henric-94; Cement 9-78; Bull-68)							
MAX (FIN)	1984	26	14,88	5,26	2,10		

Towage services at Loviisa (Valkom)

HINAUS KAIPAA OY

Nojanmaanlahdentie 25 F 28, 57210 Savonlinna, Finland
Tel : +358 50 412 8797   Fax : +358 15 520 424

KAIPAA (FIN)	1948	111	28,95	5,90	2,80	494	7.6
(ex Normand-73)							

Towage services around the Finnish archipelago and in the Saimaa lakes

HP UITTO

Muhasaarentie 5, 57100 Savonlinna, Finland

ROTEVA (FIN)	1946	61	21,40	5,20	2,20	
(ex B9 - 48; TID 169 - 47)						
TAPIO (FIN)	1960	53	19,80	4,84	2,40	7.3

Towage services in the Saimaa lakes

The Håkans fleet comprises owned and managed tugs. Two of the latter, the VIIKARI and AKILLES, both registered at Kotka, were photographed in their home port on an incredibly wet 31 August 2000.

(Bernard McCall)

OY ALFONS HÅKANS AB

Linnankatu 36 C, 20100 Turku, Finland
Tel : +358 251 555000   Fax : +358 2 251 5873
E-mail : jari.talja@alfonshakans.fi
Website : www.alfonshakans.fi

AJAX (FIN)	1950	200	28,00	8,30	4,21	2700	27.0
(ex Baba Yaga-88; Sjøbjørn-86; Sjöbjörn-70)							
CALYPSO (EST)	2004		25,86	8,94	4,35	3150	36.0
FART (FIN)	1907/60	132	27,14	6,12	3,22	1260	13.0
FRAM (FIN)	1958	270	33,00	8,82	4,86	2250	22.0
(ex Axel Enstrom-86)							
HAMLET (FIN)	1967	114	23,70	7,17	4,00	1200	15.7
(ex Tebe-88; Starkgrogg-78)							
HARALD (FIN)	1963	178	28,55	8,13	3,07	1600	18.0
(ex Karnan-88)							
HECTOR (FIN)	1975	333	33,02	9,50	4,85	3915	50.2
(ex Ingemar-03)							
HELIOS (FIN)	1976	292	34,00	9,60	3,80	3500	35.0
(ex Kwintebank-03)							
HERMES (FIN)	1976	167	25,30	8,11	3,76	2640	32.0
(ex Hermes av Uddevalla-03; Gaven-02)							

The HERMES at Rauma on 26 July 2004.

(Bernard McCall)

HURTIG (FIN)	1944	160	27,41	8,11	4,55	2000	20.0
(ex Herbert-81)							
ISO-PUKKI (FIN)	1968	243	30,50	9,03	4,20	2000	20.0
JOONAS (FIN)	1990	33	15,80	5,05	2,04	550	7.0
KRAFT (FIN)	1976	327	35,46	9,22	4,30	3520	48.0
(ex Kone-79)							
NEPTUN (EST)	1980	323	31,57	9,80	5,60	4260	37.0
(ex Heimo Saarinen-88)							

PALLAS (EST)	1976	292	34,15	9,22	5,20	3000	35.0
(ex Varnebank-04)							
PLUTO (FIN)	1958/77	96	25,88	6,22	3,25	1750	18.0
(ex Tiger Boxer-91; Eir-84; Tunö-70)							
PRIMUS (FIN)	1965	117	24,20	7,35	3,60	1000	13.0
PROTECTOR (EST)	1965	375	40,43	9,85	4,30	3685	31.0
TORVIK (FIN)	1958/80	84	22,16	6,20	3,75	1440	15.0
(ex Tor-77)							
TURSO (FIN)	1949	294	36,09	9,36	4,10	1100	14.0
TYR (FIN)	1959	135	25,31	7,68	3,80	1100	12.0
(ex Tyri-89; Tyr-80)							
WAIJA (FIN)	1916/71	140	27,30	6,84	4,00	1850	18.0
(ex Wäija-61; Svanö I-28)							
ZEUS (FIN)	1995	545	45,10	14,60	6,75	7370	101.0
Managed for City of Pori							
PORIN KARHU (FIN)	1950/75	208	32,01	9,91	4,40	3520	32.0

The managed tugs generally wear the colours of their owners rather than the scarlet and blue which are the funnel colours of the Håkans-owned tugs. The Port of Pori's PORIN KARHU has a green and cream livery whilst the HURTIG is in Håkans colours at Mantyluoto, the port of Pori, on 18 July 1999.

(Dominic McCall)

Managed for City of Rauma							
KALKKE (FIN)	1965	282	29,98	8,78	4,20	1260	15.0
Managed for Finntowatec Ltf Oy							
AKILLES (FIN)	1958	60	19,66	6,00	3,10	1400	12.5

Managed for Finntugs Oy

ATLAS (FIN)	1964/95	189	28,53	8,11	4,60	1350	13.7
(ex Herman Kubbe-95; Varangis II-74)							
VIIKARI (FIN)	1981	354	32,90	10,00	4,80	3920	39.0

Managed for Stefan A. Håkans

JASON (FIN)	1953/89	175	29,75	7,74	4,30	2180	22.0
(ex Panter-90; Merikotka-84)							

Managed for Suomen Merisukellus Oy, Rauma

BAUS (FIN)	1970	515	36,33	10,02	5,56	3200	32.0
(ex Letavor-01; Baus-99; Rauma IV-99; Hans Oscar-97; Hans Oskar-88; Baus-85)							
LIPPO (FIN)	1980	20	11,80	4,20	1,00		
PEGASOS (FIN)	1968	217	28,75	8,20	4,60	1660	22.0
(ex Rauma III-99; Björn-96)							
SAUKO (FIN)	1962	23	12,00	4,00	1,80		

Towage and icebreaking services at Hanko, Helsinki, Kantvik, Rauma and Turku.
Towage services in Estonian ports of Muuga, Tallinn and Paldiski operated by associate company Alfons Håkans OÜ, Tallinn.
Coastal towage and salvage operations in the North Sea and Baltic

ITÄ-SUOMEN HINAUS OY
Jääkiekkoradankuja 4 a 6, 57170 Savonlinna, Finland

ARSKA (FIN)	1943	60	20,75	5,30	2,40		9.0
(ex Repola 4-84; John Bull-61; B7-47; TID 41-46)							

Towage services in the Saimaa lakes

IDÄNTIE KY- ÖSTERLED KB
Tiemestarinkatu 5, 20360 Turku, Finland
Tel : +358 2 253 9502   Fax : +358 2 253 9506
E-mail : idantie@postikaista.net
Website : www.idantie.fi

AJAX (FIN)	1963	288	33,86	9,05	4,20	1660	20.0
(ex Tuggard-04; Ajax-94)							
KEMI 1 (FIN)	1976	109	25,00	6,85	2,80	600	8.5
UITTO 1 (FIN)	1965/95		12,70	4,00	3,00	360	5.2
UITTO 6 (FIN)	1963/03		14,00	4,05	2,40	430	6.0

Towage and ice breaking services in the Baltic, Finnish & Swedish water systems

JAKOBSTADS BOGSER A/B
Mäkituvankuja 8, 68600 Pietarsaari, Finland
Tel : +358 2 7244029

SIMSON (FIN)	1966	234	30,87	8,44	4,11	1680	
(ex Sim-94; Simson-94)							

Towage services at Pietarsaari (Jakobstad)

The SIMSON was photographed at her home port in June 2004.

(Jan Rautawaara)

JOUSMAA KY, K
Trolleberginite 13 PL 90, 10601 Tammisaari, Finland
Tel : +358 19 2414488
POLARIS (FIN)   1964   256   32,31   8,61   4,46   2400   22.0
(ex Tug Frisøy-04; Byteren-00; Løve-93; Sjollen-83)

JÄRVI-SUOMEN UITTOYHDISTYS
Pl 47, 57101 Savonlinna, Finland
ARVO (FIN)   1961   37   17,64   4,40   1,84   5.1
(ex Lauri II)
LAURI   1957   37   17,64   4,40   1,84   5.1
Timber towage services in the Saimaa lakes

JÄRVIKULJETUS M PAPUNEN OY
Yhdystie 18, 57200 Savonlinna, Finland
HANHI (FIN)   1921   45   18,10   4,52
(ex Repola 7 - 89; Tapio-41)
Pusher tug operating in the Saimaa lakes

KAIVINYHTYMÄ VELJET SALMINEN
Kutterintie 7, 20900 Turku, Finland
PETRA (FIN)   1954   36   16,05   4,50   2,40
(ex Mascotte)

KALLAN MATKAILU OY
Uunimaantie 18, 85180 Rahja, Finland
Tel : +358 400 382 652
E-mail : etu.sukunimi@r-towing.fi
Website : www.r-towing.fi

Operated by R-Towing Oy

POLLUX (FIN)	1956	80	25,01	6,12	3,50	887	13.0
(ex Pluto-89)							
CASTOR (FIN)	1956	89	25,01	6,12	3,25	887	13.0
(ex Iiro-89; Taru-80; Tyr-80)							
LENNE (FIN)	1961	182	29,15	7,96	4,46	1250	14.0
(ex Thetis-83; Fredsgrogg-67)							

Towage services in the Baltic, Kattegat and Skagerrak

The LENNE is seen at Vaasa on 26 July 2004 when in the ownership of Botnia Seatug whose funnel colours she was wearing. She was sold to her present owners later in 2004.

(Bernard McCall)

KEMIN KAUPUNKI - CITY OF KEMI

Satamatoimisto, Ajos, 94100 Kemi, Finland
Tel : +358 16 282017   Fax : +358 16 282003

JÄÄSALO (FIN)	1975	301	32,82	10,40	5,12	3520	34.5
ULLA (FIN)	1965	126	24,06	7,37	2,89	1330	
(ex Brage-74; Storgrogg-69)							

Towage services at Kemi

KESKINEN JUHA

Kirkkoniemenkatu 19, 57510 Savonlinna, Finland

TIKKA (FIN)	1972	64	19,75	5,60	2,50

Towage services in the Saimaa lakes

KORPIVAARA KARI

Savonlinna, Finland
TORNATOR (FIN) 1908 53 23,06 4,65 2,55
(ex Torna; Tornator-83, Tornator IV-31)

LINDHOLM KERTTU PERIKUNTA

c/o Mauri Lindholm, Kaniikintie 4, 20300 Turku, Finland
JUSSI VII (FIN) 1924 26 14,72 4,30 2,00
(ex Ajo VII-76, Stockfors III-53)
RISTO (FIN) 1912 35 18,18 4,52 2,40
(ex Ost-64)

LÄNSIHINAUS OY

Mikolantie 182, 25360 Pertteli, Finland
AURA 3 (FIN) 1950 165 29,93 7,53 3,70 650
(ex Ahava-95; Jääaura-94; Rahja-91; Vaasa-84; Aura-69)

MENTULA JUHA KY

Teollisuutie 12, 54500 Taavetti, Finland
KARALI (FIN) 1967 62 16,06 5,25
Towage services in the Saimaa lakes

MERIRAKENNUS OY

Pohjoinen Hesperiankatu 11 A 6, 00260 Helsinki, Finland
Tel : +358 9 444 951   Fax : +358 9 445 39
FREJ (FIN) 1968 250 30,48 8,40 3,61 2480 23.0
(ex Atlas-73)
RAJU (FIN) 1983 43 17,30 5,30 2,90 512 8.8
RÖNÖ (FIN) 1972 28 15,00 4,80 2,80
Towage and ice breaking services around Helsinki

MOPRO OY

PL 102, 57100 Savonlinna, Finland
Tel : +358 15 532 122   Fax : +358 15 532 200
E-mail : mopro@mopro.fi
Website : www.mopro.fi
ARPPE (FIN) 1989 351 29,40 12,50 2,80 2039 n/a
Ice-breaking and pusher services in the Saimaa lakes with the company's barge

MYRD INVEST LTD OY

Soumenkyläntie 24, 06100 Porvoo, Finland
GÖTA (FIN) 1907 55 21,06 4,92 2,40
(ex Flodsprutan)

MÄKELÄ REINO

Välikatu 1 B 21, 87100 Kajaani, Finland

JALO (FIN)	1909	38	17,27	4,30

(ex Pankakoski II)

OULUN KAUPUNKI / ULEABORGS STAD

P.O. Box 23, 90015 Oulu, Finland
Tel : +358 8 5586 2770

TUURA (FIN)	1971	364	35,49	9,85	4,92	3600

Towage services at Oulu

The TUURA at Oulu on 25 July 2004.

(Bernard McCall)

PATANEN PATU

Tervasaari, Hamina, Finland

MERIKARHU (FIN)	1943	99	24,48	6,06	2,78

(ex No. 13-48; ST. 79-46)

PERKAUS OY

PI 47, 57101 Savonlinna, Finland

CHR. KONTTURI (FIN)	1908/69	86	24,62	5,40	2,70
TARMO (FIN)	1943/83	60	21,40	5,30	2,20

(ex B1-48; TID 1-46)
Towage services in the Saimaa lakes

PIELIS-PUSKU KY
Kaarlonkatu 3, 75500 Nurmes, Finland
Tel : +358 13 480 580

JERMAC (FIN)	1970	141	25,70	7,50	3,10	1000	11.4

(ex Rauma III-89)

AUVO PITKÄNEN
Pohjanrannantie 49, 48300 Kotka, Finland
Tel : +358 400 555 133

NICO (FIN)	1983/95	41	13,75	6,00	2,60	360	13.5

PUUMALAINEN SEPPO & LIISA
Kumpulantie 8, 81280 Uimaharju, Finland

LIISA (FIN)	1943	66	21,42	5,19	2,40

(ex Kessu-88; H3 - 78; B14 - 4; TID 49 - 46)

PÄIJÄT-STEEL KY
Rosellintie 36, 17780 Harmoien, Finland

KALLE (FIN)	1960	25	14,95	4,36	1,95

(ex Martti 3)
Towage services in the Saimaa lakes

RAAHEN MERIAPU OY
Metsäpuhto 1, 92160 Saloinen, Finland
Tel : +358 400 383 697   Fax : +358 8 263 678
E-mail : raameri@p.p.kolumbus.fi

ISBJÖRN (FIN)	1964	159	24,92	8,15	4,00	1479

RAHJAN HUOLINTA OY
Satamatie 436, 85180 Rahja, Finland
Tel : +358 8 464 0880   Fax : +358 8 464 0850

MASA (FIN)	1975	123	24,49	7,38	3,60	1311	15.3

(ex Esta-03)
Towage services at Rahja

RAUMA CHARTERING & TOWING AGENCY OY AB LTD
Karjalankatu 15, 26100 Rauma, Finland
Tel : +358 2822 7900   Fax : +358 2 822 7944
E-mail : raumacata@raumacata.fi
Website : www.raumacata.fi

ALI (FIN)	1981	21	13,50	3,84	1,70	315	5.0

FANCY (FIN)	1854	22	13,90	4,00	2,19	360	6.0
METEOR (FIN)	1960/87	396	38,50	9,22	4,30	1740	20.0
(ex Parainen-01; Pellinki-81; Meteor-97)							
MINOS (FIN)	1943/84	51	22,15	5,25	1,80	375	6.5
ROLLE (FIN)	1965/01	17	14,28	3,48	1,42	335	6.0
TINTO (FIN)	1953	107	23,71	7,01	3,10	1000	12.0

(ex Stor-Joel-03; Grissly-96; Snik-91; Grissly-90; Hinna-86; Stor Viking-85; Royal-67; Assi-57)

Towage services at Rauma; also coastal towage in North Sea and Baltic

RUSI JUHANI
Kanslerintie 6 G, 20200 Turku, Finland

NICKE (FIN)	1926	26	14,74	4,19	2,38

TOPPILAN MÖLJÄ OY
Oulu, Finland

ALPO (FIN)	1943	106	24,48	6,06	2,40

(ex No. 18 - 51, ST. 335 - 46)

UITTOPOJAT OY
Korvenkatu 45, 18150 Heinola, Finland

OLLI (FIN)	1963	53	19,80	4,84	2,40	7.3

(ex Tapio II)
Towage services in the Saimaa lakes

UPM-KYMMENE OYJ METSÄ
Vesitiekuljetus, P.O. Box 1023, 53301 Lappeenranta, Finland

PARKKO (FIN)	1966	95	22,40	6,58	2,80	717

(ex Rauma I-88; Repola-87)
Towage services in the Saimaa lakes

VAASAN HINAUS - VASA BOGSERING OY AB
Kyrontie 43, 65230 Vaasa, Finland
Tel : +358 6 312 2233   Fax : +358 6 312 2233

HERCULES (FIN)	1960	161	25,35	7,85	3,90	1020	
(ex Bill-79)							
HERMANNI (FIN)			14,24	4,15	2,50		6.0
JÄÄKOTKA (FIN)	1963	298	33,96	9,30	4,35	1617	22.0

Towage services at Vaasa

VARUSTAMO HANS PALME OY
Bergvägen 3, Godby, Finland

OTTO (FIN)	1954	25	14,90	4,50	2,23

VEIROS AB

Borgå, Finland

STINA (FIN)	1963	27	14,95	4,44	2,20

(ex Martti 4-87)

The STINA gives assistance to a barge on the Kiel Canal in June 1990.

(Jan Rautawaara)

YXPILA HINAUS-BOGSERING OY AB

Herm Renlundinkatu 36 A S, 67200 Kokkola, Finland

AKKE (FIN)	1916/64	220	31,50	9,38	4,70	1381	
ORION (FIN)	1974	378	36,30	9,20	4,80	3400	35.0

(ex Björn-64; Pampus-58; Isbrytaren II-52)

(ex Breton Sea-94; Orion Expeditor-90; Orion-81)

Towage services at Kokkola

The ORION at Kokkola on 25 July 2004.

(Bernard McCall)

YIT RAKENNUS OY

PI 36, 00621 Helsinki, Finland

LEONORA (FIN)	1969	20	13,75	4,20	1,42

Ö-SKOG AB OY

Våno dalväg 222, 21600 Pargas, Finland
Tel : +358 4 0052 3738   Fax : +358 2 4587 058
E-mail : o-skog@parnet.fi
Website : www.o-skog.parnet.fi

RÖJVIK	1966	60	20,48	5,88	2,70	640	7.0

(ex Öresund-04; Breifjord)
Towage services with company's barge

UNKNOWN OWNERS

VOIKKAA (FIN)	1911/65	52	22,57	4,95

(ex Halla V-65, Sirius)

TUGS - ICELAND

AKRANESHÖFN

Faxabraut 1, 300 Akranes, Iceland
E-mail : akhofn@akranes.is
Wesbite : www.akraneshofn.is

HERCULES (ISL)	1960	54	18,00	5,21	2,30	310	
(ex Dolphin-01; Asa-98)							
LEYNIR (ISL)	2000	42	16,41	5,26	3,40	960	14.8
THJOUR (ISL)	1990	24	14,25	4,26	1,75		3.0

Coastal towage around Iceland

PORT OF REYKJAVIK

Postfang 382, Reykjavik, 121, Iceland
Tel : +354 525 8931   Fax : +354 525 8991
E-mail : ludvik@reykjavikurhofn.is
Website : www.reykjavikurhofn.is

JÖTUNN (ISL)	2001	42	16,85	5,69	2,51	960	13.2
MAGNI (ISL)	1996	76	19,50	6,04	2,58	1280	18.0

Towage services at Reykjavik

HARBOUR OF VESTMANNAEYJAR

Skildingavegur 5, 15-900 Vestmannaeyjar, Iceland
Tel : +354 481 1192   Fax : +354 481 3115
E-mail : omk@vestmannaeyjar.is
LÓDSINN (ISL)   1998   156   24,22   7,33   3,95   2029   30.0
Towage services at Vestmannaeyjar

The two tugs serving the port of Reykjavik are the MAGNI and JÖTUNN. The latter vessel also serves as a pilot cutter. Both photographs were taken on 27 July 2004.

(Jim McFaul))

AMBERHOLDING LATVIA

Āzenes iela 12, LV-1048, Rīga, Latvia

CIKLONS (LVA)	1969	180	29,30	8,49	3,16	1200	
(ex Tsiklon-92)							
DZINTAURS (LVA)	1967	179	29,30	8,49	3,20	1200	
(ex BK 1224)							
MUSONS (LVA)	1987	270	35,78	9,49	3,28	2518	
(ex Musson-91)							
PASĀTS (LVA)	1983	333	35,82	9,72	3,35	2400	32.0
(ex Galati 1-99)							
ŠIROKO (LVA)	1984	333	35,82	9,72	3,35	2400	32.0
(ex Galati 2-00)							
TAIFUNS (LVA)	1972	180	29,30	8,49	3,90	1200	
(ex Tayfun-92)							

Managed for Amber Holding LLC

VĒTRA (LVA)	2000	330	35,81	9,71	3,35	2400	

Towage services at Riga

A splendid view of the CIKLONS working at the Latvian port of Liepaja in very wintry conditions on 9 January 2003. The photographer was grateful for the sunlight which certainly enhanced the scene.

(Barry Standerline)

LIEPAJA SPECIAL ECONOMIC ZONE AUTHORITY
Feniksa iela 4, LV-3400 Liepāja, Latvia
Tel : +371 34 27356
E-mail : port@lsez.lv
Website : www.liepaja-sez.lv

NĀMĒJS (LVA)	1969	181	27,92	8,56	3,67	1500	32.0

(ex Bugsier 33-93)
Towage and marine servcies at Liepaja

SIA "LIG-M"
Lielupes iela 48/2-4, LV-1016 Rīga, Latvia

MARSS (LVA)	1977	186	29,36	8,49	3,34	1200

(ex Mars-00)

PLUTONS (LVA)	1962	184	29,30	8,50	3,09	1200

(ex Saturn-01; BK 1201)
Towage services in Latvia

LTS
37a, Tvaika iela, Rīga, Latvia

JUPITERS (EST)	2003	618	31,80	9,70	4,20	3300

(ex Jupiter-04)
Towage services in Latvia

OSTAS FLOTE LTD
20A, Dzintaru iela, LV-3602 Ventspils, Latvia
Tel : +371 36 61955   Fax : +371 36 63022
E-mail : secretary@of.vcp.lv
Website : www.vcp.lv
Livery - Black hull with mustard housing and wheelhouse; black funnel with white band

ALIOTS (LVA)	1978	186	29,30	6,40	3,50	1200	
(ex Neptun-92)							
ARKTURS (LVA)	1983	270	35,83	9,10	3,15	2520	33.0
(ex Lachplesis-92)							
FOBOS (LVA)	1975	111	24,20	6,95	3,38	900	
(ex Merkuriy-92)							
MARSS 1 (LVA)	1982	728	39,60	12,00	6,10	5040	75.0
(ex Mars-93)							
TEODORS SPADE (LVA)	1988	270	35,78	9,49	4,39	2520	33.0
(ex Burun-96)							
VENTSPILS (LVA)	2000	305	30,82	10,20	4,80	3500	45.0

Towage services at Ventspils

RIGA SHIP REPAIR YARD
Gāles iela 2, LV-1015 Rīga, Latvia
Tel : +371 7 353433   Fax : +371 7 353452
E-mail : riga@riga-shipyard.com
Website : www.riga-shipyard.com

NIKOLAJS NEČIPORENKO (LVA) (ex Nikolay Nechiporenko-92)	1974	178	29,30	8,49	3,09	1200
TRIKS (LVA) (ex Antey-92)	1971	178	28,81	7,10	3,65	1200

Towage services at Riga shipyard

TANDEM LTD
Fabrikas iela 2, LV-3610 Ventspils, Latvia

TANDEM (LVA) (ex Soru-92; Sever-92)	1953	122	28,75	6,20	

Towage services in Latvia

TUGS - LITHUANIA

The STUMBRAS at her home port of Klaipeda.

(Alastair Paterson)

KLAIPEDA STATE SEAPORT AUTHORITY
24, Julius Janonio, LT-92251 Klaipėda, Lithuania
Tel : +370 46 499 799   Fax : +370 46 499 777
E-mail : info@port.lt
Website : www.portofklaipeda.lt
Managed by KLASCO (Lithuania)

STUMBRAS (LTU)	2000	313	30,82	10,02	4,80	4196	51.0

Towage services at Klaipeda

KLAIPEDA STEVEDORING CO. (KLASCO)
Zauerveino g. 18, LT-92122 Klaipėda, Lithuania
Tel : +370 46 399 101   Fax : +370 46 399 066
E-mail : towage@klasco.lt
Website : www.klasco.lt

BARTA (LTU)	1989	182	29,30	8,60	3,40	1580	20.0
BIZONAS (LTU)	1980	281	35,83	9,30		2480	31.5
(ex Bizon-92)							
SEMBA (LTU)	1984	182	29,32	8,62	3,40	1580	20.4
(ex Neris)							

Towage and stevedore services at Klaipeda

JSSC "KLAIPĖDOS SMELTĖ"
Nemuno g. 24, LT-5799 Klaipėda, Lithuania
Tel : +370 46 496201   Fax : +370 46 496230
E-mail : info@smelte.lt
Website : www.smelte.lt

GINTARAS (LTU)	1973	186	29,30	8,31	3,71	1200	14.0
SVYTURYS (LTU)	1976	186	29,30	8,50	3,73	1200	14.0
(ex Shvituris-92)							

Towage and stevedore services at Klaipeda

TOWAGE & MARINE ASSISTANCE
S Daukanto g. 3, LT-92123 Klaipėda, Lithuania
Tel : +370 46 303 427   Fax : +370 46 303 428
E-mail : info@towage.lt
Website : www.towage.lt
Livery : Red hull, white housing and wheelhouse.

TAK 9 (LTU)	1995	408	34,00	10,60	4,00	4000	50.0
(ex Boa Tor-04; Birk-99; Boa Tor-98)							

Managed for Neue Schleppdampfschiffsreederei Louis Meyer (Germany)

TAK 2 (LTU)	1959	132	26,86	7,23	3,60	1000	20.0
(ex Ernst-97; Johanna-73)							
TAK 3 (LTU)	1979	159	24,08	8,55	4,50	1500	20.0
(ex John-98)							

An interesting view of the TAK 5 at Klaipeda on 13 July 2004. Clearly visible behind her is the SVITZER MJØLNER under construction.

(Ron Wood)

TAK 5 (LTU)	1972	181	26,07	8,84	2,80	1739	29.0
(ex Jan-99; Bugsier 2-97)								

Managed for Petersen & Alpers (Germany)

TAK 1 (LTU)	1975	181	26,17	8,80	4,80	1739	29.0
(ex Ise-98; Courageux-98; Ise-87)								
TAK 4 (LTU)	1980	207	26,74	8,80	4,80	1739	27.0
(ex Johanna-97)								

Towage services at Klaipeda and in the surrounding area

TUGS - NORWAY

KÅRE BERG
P.O.Box 323, N-1753 Halden, Norway
Mobile tel : + 47 900 97 601

LOKRAFT (NOR)	1939/67	128	25,56	7,02		850	14.0
(ex Storgrogg-00; Big-96; Melløs II-90; Voima-86; Runskär-83)							

BORA SANDFRAKT AS

6060 Hareid, Norway
Tel : +47 70 09 33 88   Fax : +47 70 09 33 88

GREVEN (NOR)	1953	46	18,44	4,54		300	5.0
OSKAR (NOR)	1952	78	23,73	5,73	2,07	440	6.0

(ex Nordryggen-93)

BRAVO TUG AS

Alfabyget, 5392 Storebø, Norway
Tel/Fax : +47 56 18 10 00
Livery - Black hull with white housing and funnels

NORDIC BRAVO (VCT)	1997	223	29,00	8,60	3,50	2500	34.0

(ex Bravo-99; PM 204-97)
Towage services towing fresh water bags

AS BUKSERBÅTER

Havnegata 28, 8514 Narvik, Norway
Tel : +47 76 92 38 00   Fax : +47 76 94 49 25
Livery - Black hull with brown winches and deck, white housing and wheelhouse; buff funnel

RALLAREN (NOR)	1973	503	36,23	11,41	3,70	3600	43.0
ROMBAK (NOR)	1976	506	36,23	11,41	3,70	3900	47.0
SVARTA BJØRN (NOR)	1962	279	35,49	9,17	4,32	3280	23.0

Towage services at Narvik

A photograph with an international flavour. The Copenhagen-registered but Norwegian-owned BAMSE TUG is seen in the New Waterway near Rotterdam.

(Ferry van Rijsbergen)

BUKSÉR OG BERGING AS

PO Box 1534, Vika N-0117 Oslo, Norway
Tel : +47 23 11 63 50   Fax : +47 23 11 63 51
E-mail : bukser@bube.no
Website : www.bube.no
Livery - Red hull, white housing & wheelhouse with red band round top; black funnel with company logo

(tbn) (NOR)	2005		40,60	14,50			95.0
(tbn) (NOR)	2005		36,00	13,00			75.0
(tbn) (NOR)	2005		36,00	13,00			75.0
BAMSE TUG (DIS)	1985	370	35,00	9,80	5,30	4845	69.0
(ex Bamse-03)							
BAUT (NOR)	2003	741	40,55	14,30	5,80	9382	95.0
BEBE (NOR)	1964/92	140	26,82	7,49	3,43	1925	23.0
BENI (NOR)	1962	84	25,27	6,72	3,30	2200	22.0
(ex Torian-88; Riverman-78)							
BESS (NOR)	1994	498	36,00	12,00	5,00	5448	55.0
BJØNN (NOR)	1969	136	25,66	7,50	3,46	1200	15.0
BOB (SWE)	1997	475	35,15	12,40	5,28	5168	52.0
BOXER (NOR)	1999	682	38,85	13,70	6,00	6794	67.0
BRUSE (SWE)	1981	295	29,42	9,55	5,80	2500	39.0
(ex Camp-94; Camp 1-82)							
BUKKEN (NOR)	1982	295	29,20	9,50	5,80	2500	35.0
(ex Tug-92)							
BULLDOG (NOR)	1999	481	35,00	11,50	5,20	5500	65.0
JOHN (NOR)	1991	344	32,89	10,20	4,60	4000	53.0
(ex John af Göteborg-99; Portunus-93; John af Göteborg-91)							
LARS (NOR)	1893/73	83	23,50	6,00	4,00	1100	15.0
(ex Matre-60; Nesfoss-60; Tordenskjold-51)							
VULCANUS (NOR)	1959	142	27,92	7,01	3,66	960	16.0

The BISON is seen at full speed near Haugesund.

(Martin Penwright)

Managed for Neptun Rederi AS (Norway)

BALDER (NOR)	1975	181	20,68	8,23	4,85	5280	35.0
BELOS (NOR)	1999	436	32,40	11,40	4,60	4120	40.0
BEVER (NOR)	1974	184	26,17	8,84	4,80	1740	29.0
(ex Peter-82)							
BISON (NOR)	1981	300	30,00	9,50	5,90	3124	43.0
BULLWORKER (NOR)	1973	640	53,64	11,58	2,84	2282	20.0
(ex Mikal I-02; Forties Moon-86)							
HAABULL (NOR)	1978	253	27,70	8,80	6,00	2550	35.0

Towage services at various ports and oil terminals in Norway; coastal towage and salvage

CONTINENTAL SHIP MANAGEMENT A/S

P. O.Box 1281, N-5508 Karmsund, Norway
Tel : +47 52 84 80 00   Fax : +47 52 84 80 01
E-mail : services@continentalship.com
Website : www.continentalship.com

NESBOY (BRB)	1989	122	26,80	6,20	2,50	565	9.3

LARS RAGNVALD DJUPEVÅG

Vikøyvegen 593, N-5600 Norheimsund, Norway
Tel. :+ 47 56 55 27 67

KOLBJØN (NOR)	1898/63	48	19,20	5,03	2,77	465	6.0

DRAMMEN HAVNEVESEN

Hans Kiærsgate 1A, 3041 Drammen, Norway
Tel : +47 32 20 86 50   Fax : +47 32 20 86 51
Website : www.drammenhavn.no

Managed by Bukser og Berging AS (Norway)

THOR III (NOR)	1960	292	35,08	9,32	4,55	1430	17.0

Towage and marine services at Drammen

DRØBAK MARINE SERVICE

Gylteveien 16, 1440 Drøbak, Norway
Tel : +47 64 93 44 47   Fax : +47 64 93 47 80
Livery - Black hull, white wheelhouse with orange trim

GYLTINGEN (NOR)	1979	25	14,73	4,18	2,00	365	7.0

(ex Einar Senior-93; Wegreto-88)
Marine services at Drøbak

DS TURISTEN AS

Lund Gård, N-1798 Aremark, Norway

THOR (NOR)	1904	42	19,48	4,60		549	6.0

(ex Tor-98; Thor-41)
A preserved vessel no longer in commercial service

EIDE MARINE SERVICES A/S

Roysanes, 5457 Hoylandsbygd, Norway
Tel : +47 53 48 35 00   Fax : +47 53 47 72 40
E-mail : georg.eide@eide-gruppen.no
Website : www.eide-gruppen.no
Livery - Light blue hull with white housing and wheelhouse

EIDE FOX (NOR)		1957	97	26,20	6,70	2,80	575	8.0
(ex Tott-88; Ajax-87)								
EIDE MAX (NOR)		1962/94	164	30,60	7,45	3,50	1000	17.0
(ex Amrum-94)								
EIDE REX (NOR)		1975	330	38,15	9,20	4,50	2640	38.0
(ex Duchray-98)								
EIDE TRAVELER (NOR)		1977	1389	63,91	13,31	5,34	7360	92.0
(ex Motorman-04; Searcher-02; Smit-Lloyd 119-98; Biehi Traveler-91)								
MERCHANTMAN (NOR)		1975	1388	63,91	13,29	5,06	7200	100.0
(ex Achiever-01; Smit-Lloyd 115-98)								

Coastal towage around Norway; also operate floating crane vessels

The EIDE MAX seen south of Bergen.

(James Dodds)

ARNT ENEBAKK AS

Ternevegen 21, 8550 Lodingen, Norway
Tel : +47 76 93 13 56   Fax : +47 76 93 17 05
Livery - Black hull, buff housing and wheelhouse; black funnel

NORDBEVER (NOR)		1962/88	188	30,75	8,28	3,58	1750	22.0
(ex Westgarth-81; Duncurlew-71; Westgarth-62)								

FARSUND FORTØYNINGSSELSKAP AS

Lilletjonn Terrasse 3, 4550 Farsund, Norway
Tel : +47 38 39 12 29   Fax : +47 38 39 31 40
E-mail : mail@ffs-as.com
Website : www.ffs-as.com

FARØY (NOR)			17,60	4,91	2,50	300	
KHAN (NOR)	1967/97	235	32,13	8,07	4,20	1700	26.0

(ex Argus-00; Mor-97; Coburg-93; Alfred Lamey-70)
Towage services at Farsund; also coastal towage

FJORD SHIPPING AS

PO Box F, 6701 Måløy, Norway (or Gate 1 nr 98, 6700 Måløy, Norway)
Tel : +47 57 85 38 50   Fax : +47 57 85 38 60
E-mail : post@fjordshipping.com
Website : www.fjordshipping.com

Managed for Porto Shipping Ltd

TUG MERCUR (NIS)	1964	324	38,71	9,20	4,70	2760	
(ex Mercur-00)							
TUG NESTOR (NIS)	1972	236	29,11	8,97	4,30	1951	27.0

(ex Nestor-00)
Towage services at Måløy and coastal towage.

The TUG NESTOR was photographed in the Estonian port of Kunda in July 2004.

(Jan Rautawaara)

FORSVARETS LOGISTIKK ORGANISASJON (FLOSJO) (ROYAL NORWEGIAN NAVY LOGISTICS ORGANISATION)

P. O.Box 3 Haakonsvern, N-5886 Bergen, Norway
Tel : +47 55 50 20 00

MJØLNER (NOR)	2002	247	23,99	9,00	3,53	3000	42.0
(ex Boa Mjølner-02)							
SLEIPNER (NOR)	2002	247	23,99	9,00	3,53	3000	40.0
(ex Boa Sleipner-02)							

HAMMERFEST HAVNEVESEN KF

Postboks 123, 9615 Hammerfest, Norway
Tel : +47 78 40 74 00   Fax : +47 78 40 74 01
E-mail : post@hammerfest.havn.no

VESTVERN (NOR)	1978	49	14,95	6,00	2,20	500	7.5

Towage services at Hammerfest

HANSON SJØTRANSPORT AS

6480 Aukra, Norway
Tel : +47 71 17 46 95   Fax : +47 71 17 46 95
E-mail : jhanson@online.no

RUSKEN (NOR)	1936	82	23,85	6,25	760	10.0

OLLE HECTOR

Mosseveien 217, 1169 Oslo, Norway
Tel/Fax : +47 22 28 38 73
Managed for Borre AS

BØRRE (NOR)	1947/71	108	27,88	6,33	3,20	1320	15.0
(ex Cement 8-00; Bergslep I-00; Bergslep-00; Big-86)							

HYDROTECH-GRUPPEN AS

Bentnesveien 50, N-6512 Kristiansund N, Norway

TRAVACO (NOR)	1988	14,99	5,70	510	10.0

ICE LADY AS

Havnedalsvn. 4, 9990 Batsfjord, Norway
Tel : +47 78 98 33 63   Fax : +47 78 98 37 32

TERRY (NOR)	1964	58	18,50	5,01	3,35	1028	13.0

Towage services at Vardø

ALF JOHNSEN SLIPP & MEK VERKSTED
5423 Brandasund, Norway
Tel/Fax : +47 53 42 95 48

HUTH (NOR)	1904/69	98	24,50	6,10	4,00	1420	17.0
(ex Fredrikstad-67)							
SKRUBBEN (NOR)	1954	65	21,90	5,60	2,85	470	8.0
(ex Bugsier 10-00; Taucher O. Wulf 9-00)							

KIRKENES HAVN, SOR-VARANGER KOMMUNE
Radhusplassen, P.O. Box 406, 9915 Kirkenes, Norway
Tel : +47 78 97 74 99   Fax : +47 78 97 75 88
E-mail : post@kirkenes-havn.no
Livery - Orange hull, white housing with orange trim

KRAFT JOHANSSEN (NOR)	1974	197	28,71	8,13	3,90	2250	27.0

Towage at Kirkenes

TROND A KITTILSEN SHIPPING AS
9, Froyasvei, Stathelle 3960, Norway
Tel : +47 35 57 17 60   Fax : +47 35 57 16 97

BANGSUND (NOR)	1960	132	25,10	7,04	3,40	820	13.0
VRANGSUND (NOR)	1972	262	32,38	8,99	4,65	2400	34.0
(ex Kendal-95; Hua Lung-79)							

Coastal towage around Norway and northern Europe

ELGAR KLEPPE
6080 Gurskøy, Norway
Mobile tel : 996 22 309

FADER'N (NOR)	1957	98	26,07	6,28		715
(ex Staupfos-88)						

SIGMUND KOLSRUD
P.O. Box 1795 Nordnes, 5816 Bergen, Norway

KOBBEN (NOR)	1901/65	48	18,53	4,97	2,80	725	7.0

KRISTIANSAND EURO-PORT NORWAY
P. O. Box 3, 4661 Kristiansand S, Norway
Tel : +47 38 12 50 00   Fax : +47 38 02 70 99

OLSEN (NOR)	1990	127	29,40	6,27	2,1	832	n/a
(ex Forte-99; Zovushtchyi-93)							

Operating with barges around Scandinavia

KRISTIANSUND TAUBÅTSERVICE A/S
3, Svabergan, 6507 Kristiansund, Norway
Tel : +47 71 67 95 30
E-mail : kr-st@online.no
Website : www.dmp.no/kts
Livery - Black hull with white housing; black funnel with white stripe

WATERBJORN (NOR)	1973	184	28,07	8,24	2,80	1740	29.0
(ex Bugsier 4-97)							
WATERMAN (NOR)	1974	179	26,72	8,80	2,80	1740	29.0
(ex Bugsier 10-99)							

Towage services at Kristiansund

KVERNHUSVIK SKIPSVERFT AS
7250 Melandsjø, Norway
Tel : +47 72 44 49 80   Fax : +47 72 44 49 84
Website : www.kvernhusvik.no

STOKKÅS (NOR)	1962	46	17,00	5,00	3,00	300	6.0
ØY-KRAFT (NOR)	1938/78	136	29,00	7,10		1035	16.0
(ex Samson-94; Nathurn-48)							
ØYVÅG (NOR)	1956	133	28,19	6,91	3,32	1740	25.0
(ex Hadarvåg-00; Tranevaag-87; Mimer-85; Rex-74; Norderney-70)							

LEKTERTRANSPORT AS
Ole Deviks vei 26, 0666 Oslo, Norway
Mobile tel : 909 23 700

PORS (NOR)	1941	63	20,27	5,78	2,75	750	10.0
(ex Ole Jacob-77; Troll-61)							

MARITIME SUPPORT AS
Kommandørveien 16 B, 4085 Hundvåg, Norway

RONDO (NOR)	1975	45	14,80	5,32		750	10.0

MØRLAND & KARLSEN AS
Postboks 974 Birkenlund, 4859 Arendal, Norway
Tel : +47 37 00 59 60   Fax : +47 37 00 59 61
E-mail : mail@m-k.no
Website : www.m-k.no

HAVSØY (NOR)	1896	49	18,87	5,06		600	8.0
(ex Risøygutt-97; Rolf-94)							
MÆRDØ (NOR)	1957	98	23,98	6,49	3,50	650	7.0
(ex Bele-98)							
SKILSØ (NOR)	1958	148	27,92	7,01	3,32	1250	16.0
(ex Ursus-04; Titan-89)							

Towage services at Arendal; also coastal towage

KNUT BIRGER NILSEN
Paul Holmsensvei 77 B, 1613 Fredrikstad, Norway
Tel : +47 69 39 62 40   Fax : +47 69 39 61 80

ISEGRAN (NOR)	1939/61	79	23,73	5,73	1,93	360	5.0

(ex Svelviksand-90; Anger-49; Scheibenhof-48)

YNGVAR NILSEN
Smedebuktveien 43, N-3770 Kragerø, Norway
Tel : +47 35 98 01 98

EIK (NOR)	1936	49	23,75	5,00	2,80	600	6.0

(ex Nordmark)

NORDLANDSKE AS
P. O. Box 824, N-8001 Bodø, Norway
Tel : +47 75 50 05 00   Fax : +47 75 50 05 10
Website : www.auksjon.no

SEA REX (NOR)	1958	105	26,40	6,62	2,80	600	7.0

(ex Eide Rex-96; Knoll-88; Achilles-87)

NORDSLEP AS
Nordkappgt. 8, 9750 Honningsvåg, Norway
Tel : +47 78 47 70 73   Fax : +47 78 47 70 76

AMAZON (NOR)	1929/80	152	25,30	6,54	3,24	1155	15.0

(ex Storebirger-82; Vastervik-75)

NORSK VETERANSKIBSLUB
Postboks 1287, Vika, 0111 Oslo, Noway
Tel : +47 22 41 70 41

STYRBJORN (NOR)	1910	166	28,56	6,96		296	

(ex Atlet-80; Styrbjorn-63)
Preserved coal-fired tug no longer in commercial service

NORTH SALVOR AS
c/o Svein Sørdal, N-6410 Syvde, Norway

OCEAN LADY (CYP)	1943	290	40,89	7,56	3,78	3560	43.0

(ex Ocean Chief-04; Boa Chief-03; Eide Chief-93; Jomi-90; Uller-72; Topdalsfjord II-45)
Ocean towage services worldwide

ØYSTEIN OLAV NØSS
Utgjerdet 13, 5200 Os, Norway

HURUM (NOR)	1965	44	19,90	5,20	2,20	400	6.0

JAN EINAR OLSEN
7940 Ottersøy, Norway
Mobile tel : 911 63 335

BIRGER (NOR)	1947	99	25,40	6,20	1250	
LOFJELL (NOR)	1936/69	81	22,10	5,50	600	7.0

(ex Vaksdal-00; Lofjell-98; Duga-94; Lofjell-91; Namdalingen-80; Birger-75; Matre-69; Vaksdal-60)

OSLO HAVNEVESEN
P.O. Box 230 Sentrum, 0103 Oslo, Norway
Tel : +47 22 91 00 00   Fax : +47 2291 00 01
E-mail : liv.haddeland@ohv.oslo.no
Website : www.ohv.oslo.no
Livery - Dark blue hull with light blue wheelhouse

MJØLNER (NOR)	2001	104	18,50	7,40	1442	20.1

Towage and marine services at Oslo

RANA HAVNEVESEN
Postboks 185, N-8601 Mo-i-Rana, Norway
Tel : +47 75 13 47 00   Fax : +47 75 13 47 01
E-mail : havna@rana.kommune.no

TORANES (NOR)	1978	63	18,50	5,80	3,00	850	12.0

(ex Torani-85)
Towage and marine services at Mo-i-Rana

RIEBER SHIPPING AS
P.O. Box 1114 Sentrum, N-5809 Bergen, Norway
Tel : +47 55 59 96 00   Fax : +47 55 59 96 05
E-mail : market@polarship.no
Website : www.polarship.no

POLAR PEVEK	2006		74,36	17,00	6,00	13600

Ice-breaking and towage services at DeKrasti Oil Terminal, Sakhalin, Russia

SANDAR TANKTRANSPORT AS
Stakkevollvn. 61, 9010 Tromsø, Norway
Tel : +47 77 66 50 70   Fax : +47 77 66 50 71
E-mail : firmapost@sandar-as.no
Website : www.sandar-as.no

CHANKO (NOR)	1961	159	24,18	7,72	3,70	1260	16.0

(ex Ägir-01)
Towage services at Tromsø

SELØY KYSTBEREDSKAP AS

8850 Herøy, Norway
Tel : +47 75 05 97 50   Fax : +47 75 05 97 51
E-mail : adm@seloy.no
Website : www.seloy.no

NAUTILUS MAMMUT (NOR)	1972	99	22,49	6,73	2,99	1740	25.0

(ex Roxo-02; Haabrand-85)
Marine and underwater services around Norway

SKIP OG SERVICE AS

Fjordveien 2, N-1794 Sponvika, Norway
Tel : +47 69 19 43 90   Fax : +47 69 19 46 82

HERBERT (NOR)	1966	190	28,19	8,00	4,50	1320	15.0

(ex Janus-04; Geeste-92)

HERCULES (NOR)	1966	28	15,43	5,50	1,95	320	4.0

(ex Neuwerk-87)

SLEPEBÅTENE AS

P. O. Box 330, 9254 Tromsø, Norway
Tel : +47 77 68 25 70   Fax : +47 77 68 17 85

LARUS (NOR)	1960	116	26,80	6,60	3,40	990	11.0

(ex Frode-00)

LUPUS (NOR)	1972	276	33,00	9,60	2,70	3000	30.0

(ex Banjaardsbank-03)
Towage services at Tromsø

SØDRA CELL TOFTE AS

Tofte, 3482 Tofte, Norway
Tel : +47 32 79 90 00   Fax : +47 32 79 90 95
Managed by Bukser og Berging AS (Norway)

TOFTE II (NOR)	1980	177	24,21	8,52	3,65	2400	n/a

Barge handling services in Norway

TAUBÅTKOMPANIET AS

Pir II, 13A, Kai 9, N-7010 Trondheim, Norway.
Tel : +47 73 99 11 99   Fax : +47 73 99 11 98
E-mail : office@boa.no
Website : www.boa.no

BOA MASTER (NOR)	1994	359	30,00	9,85	4,20	4000	53.0

(ex Cinhco-97)

BOA SIW (NOR)	1976	286	33,30	9,20	3,37	3340	43.0

(ex Cheng Chau-95; Tiger Orchid-82)

The BOA SIW arrives at Aberdeen towing a barge on 21 May 2002.

BUSTER (NOR)	1956	133	28,19	6,90	3,10	1080	
(ex Juist-73)							
CHIEF (NOR)	1979	98	19,70	6,51	3,89	1125	17.0
TAMBUR (NOR)	1958/88	134	25,51	7,14	3,60	1640	20.0
(ex Traust-75)							

Towage services around Norway; also barge and salvage services

TELAS HOLDINGS AS
Grotvagen, 7200 Kyrksaeterora, Norway
Tel : +47 72 45 28 00   Fax : +47 72 45 28 01

SEUT (NOR)	1958	133	28,19	6,91	3,50	1386	19.0
(ex Kattland-94; Fru Olsen-89; Michael I-85; Spiekeroog-74)							
TELSTAR (NOR)	1930/77	98	24,60	6,08		1400	17.0
(ex Mammut-03)							

TRONDHJEM BUGSER AS
Pir II no.10, P.O. Box 196; 7401 Trondheim, Norway
Tel : +47 73 50 24 77   Fax : +47 73 50 24 78

ABRAMIS (NOR)	1982	226	28,48	3,26	3,25	2480	32.0
(ex Al Minsaf-99)							
SQUALUS (NOR)	1967	253	32,99	8,60	3,80	1800	20.0

Towage services at Trondheim; also coastal towage

ØDEGAARD BERGING AS

Skarbovik, 6006 Ålesund, Norway
Tel : +47 70 10 25 25   Fax : +47 70 10 25 30
E-mail : odegaard@berging.no
Website : www.berging.no
Livery - Red hull, white housing, with black trim; black funnel with company logo

MAMMUT TUG	(NOR)	1956	103	24,44	6,00	2,87	750	11.0
MAX MAMMUT	(NOR)	1976	229	27,87	8,20	4,25	2700	31.0
(ex Bulldog-98)								
MINI MAMMUT	(NOR)	1990	65	19,05	6,05	2,30	1360	18.0
(ex Kristine-98)								
MULTI MAMMUT	(NOR)	1976	190	26,36	8,22	4,14	2430	35.0
(ex Haabas-00)								

Towage services at Ålesund and coastal towage; also operate floating crane vessels

A colourful view of the MULTI MAMMUT at Haugesund on 30 August 2004.

(Martin Penwright)

ØSTENSJØ REDERI A/S

Smedesundet 97B, 5525 Haugesund, Norway
Tel : +47 52 70 45 45   Fax : +47 52 70 45 50
E-mail : post@ostensjo.no
Website : www.ostensjo.no
Livery - Dark blue hull, light blue housing & wheelhouse; dark blue funnel with white band
and company logo

(tbn)	(NOR)	2005		37,00	14,00	3,70	6530	65.0

AJAX (NOR)	2000	1032	41,60	15,90	6,80	10188	92.0
AUDAX (NOR)	1988	429	35,10	10,80	5,02	4400	57.0
DUX (NOR)	1985	315	29,70	9,00	5,70	3000	40.0
FELIX (NOR)	1995	397	30,80	11,14	4,78	4004	50.0
(ex Atlantic Spruce-97)							
FOX (NOR)	1988		11,15	4,25	1,90	300	4.0
PAX (NOR)	1985	315	29,70	9,00	5,70	3000	40.0
REX (NOR)	1988		11,15	4,25	1,90	300	4.0
THORAX (NOR)	1993	1229	35,80	13,80	6,30	7174	90.0
VELOX (NOR)	2004		37,00	14,00	3,70	6530	65.0
VIVAX (NOR)	1988	429	35,10	10,80	5,00	4400	57.0

The DUX was photographed near Haugesund.

(Martin Penwright)

Managed for Torksey Ltd of Douglas (IOM)							
ASTERIX (IOM)	2001	31	13,00	4,80	1,90	300	9.5
IBEX (IOM)	1993	33	14,40	4,73	1,50	600	7.6
SILEX (IOM)	1994	543	35,10	10,80	5,00	5380	62.0
THRAX (IOM)	1994	543	35,10	10,80	5,00	4895	62.0
Managed by Lee Towage Ltd (Ireland)							
ALEX (IRL)	1995	397	30,80	11,14	4,78	4004	50.0
(ex Atlantic Fir-97)							
On bareboat charter to Manwijs (Qatar)							
LAVAN (BHS)	1988	429	35,10	10,80	5,00	4400	57.0
(ex Tenax-03)							
SIRI (BHS)	1988	429	35,10	10,80	5,00	4400	57.0
(ex Velox-03)							

Towage services at various ports and oil terminals in Norway and elsewhere in Europe.

Several of the tugs in the Østensjø fleet are based at oil terminals outside Norway including, at the time of publication, the ALEX which is based at Cobh to serve the Whitegate refinery and the THRAX and SILEX which are based at Fawley on Southampton Water. Fleetmate THORAX was not too far from the latter two tugs when she was photographed as she departed from Portsmouth on 14 June 2005.

(Danny Lynch)

UNKNOWN OWNERS

HERA	1964		15,00	4,80	2,36	400	
(ex Wilanne-02; Anny B II-89; Anny B-84; No. 20)							
HOIEVARDE	1959	35	17,06				
(ex Red Knight-03; Columbus-95; Wilhelmina 8-69)							
Privately owned and converted to a yacht							
LOFJORD (NOR)	1952	99	23,00	6,62		1100	10.0
(ex Torefors-80; Wargon-70)							
Out of commercial service							
OLAF	1983	23	14,75	4,70	2,38	360	5.5
(ex Pionjar)							

TUGS - POLAND

DRAGMOR SP. Z O.O.

ul ks. St. Kujota 18-21, 70-952 Szczecin, Poland
Tel : +48 462 2396   Fax : +48 462 4785
Website : www.dragmor.com.pl

GRZEGORZ (POL)	1964	121	28,76	6,50	2,60	400	5.5

Dredging support and marine services around Poland

PORT OF GDANSK AUTHORITY
(ZARZĄD MORSKIEGO PORTU GDAŃSK SA)

ul Zamknieta 18, 80-955 Gdansk, Poland
Tel : +48 58 737 91 00   Fax : +48 58 737 94 85
Website : www.portgdansk.pl

STRAŻAK-3 (POL)	1965	112	32,16	5,92	1,73	540
STRAŻAK-5 (POL)	1976	276	37,32	9,78	2,62	2700

Towage and fire-fighting services at Gdansk

PORT OF GDYNIA AUTHORITY

Rotterdamska 9, PO Box 225, 81-337, Gdynia, Poland
Tel : +48 58 627 4036   Fax : +48 58 627 4578
E-mail : marketing@port.gdynia.pl
Website : www.port.gdynia.pl

ACHILLE (POL)	1956	146	30,10	7,04	3,20	1000
*STRAŻAK-11 (POL)	1965	112	32,12	5,92	1,70	540
*STRAŻAK-14 (POL)	1977	276	37,34	10,01	3,10	2700
WILK (POL)	1964	116	25,48	6,81	3,20	670

Towage and marine services at Gdynia
* Dedicated fire-fighting vessels

Built as a fire-fighting tug, the STRAŻAK-14 is seen at Gdynia on 28 July 2002.

(Dominic McCall)

MORSKA SŁUŻBA POSZUKIWANIA I RATOWNICTW

ul Hryniewickiego 10, 81-340 Gdynia, Poland
Tel : +48 58 661 5222   Fax : +48 58 620 5338
E-mail : office@polratok.com.pl
Website : www.polratok.com.pl
Livery - Black hull with mustard coloured housing and wheelhouse

KAPITAN POINC	(POL)	1996	1347	53,00	13,60	4,80	5200	74.0

Emergency towage and pollution services in Poland

The KAPITAN POINC is seen at Gdynia on 28 July 2002.

(Dominic McCall)

POLSKIE RATOWNICTWO OKRETOWE

ul Miodowa 26, 81-558 Gydnia, Poland
Tel : +48 58 661 1815   Fax : +48 58 664 993
E-mail : biuro@progdynia.pl
Website : www.progdynia.pl
Livery - Black hull with mustard coloured housing and wheelhouse

ENGLISHMAN	(BHS)	1975	1782	70,00	14,00	6,30	9640	122.0
(ex Schepelsturm-95)								
JANTAR	(MLT)	1979	668	44,75	11,40	7,00	4800	65.0
(ex Pacific Salvor-01; Abeille Bretagne-96)								
KORAL	(MLT)	1976	481	36,00	10,10	5,20	4400	65.0
(ex Rosscan Power-98; Stril Power-94; Bulbai-87; Stril Power-86)								
POSEJDON	(POL)	1979	1180	58,00	12,70	4,70	3500	40.0

Deep sea towage worldwide

The JANTAR passes the Hook of Holland with Europoort in the background.

(Martin Penwright)

The URAN makes her way up the Bristol Channel on 30 May 2005. She was towing a barge on which was a new crane to be installed at Royal Portbury Dock, Bristol.

(Danny Lynch)

PORT-HOL SP. Z O.O.

ul Nabrzeze Władysława IV 3, 72-600 Świnoujście, Poland
Tel : +48 91 322 3240   Fax : +48 91 321 0446
E-mail : sekretariat@porthol.co.pl
Website : www.porthol.com.pl

MINOTAUR (POL)	1975	184	29,29	8,31	4,20	1200	14.0
SAMSON (POL)	1966	227	31,60	8,40	3,60	1500	18.0
URAN (POL)	2001	313	30,82	10,20	4,70	4520	54.0
Managed for Zarząd Portu Szczecin-Świnoujście SA							
ARGUS (POL)	1976	336	36,00	10,00	5,20	2500	34.0
ATLANT (POL)	1976	336	36,00	10,00	5,20	2500	34.0

Towage services at Szczecin-Świnoujście and in the Baltic

PRZEDSIĘBIORSTWO ROBÓT CZERPALNYCH I PODWODNYCH SPOŁKA Z O.O. (PRCIP)

ul Przetoczna 66, 80-702 Gdańsk, Poland
Tel : +48 58 307 3933   Fax : +48 58 307 3745
E-mail : marketing@prcip.pl
Website : www.prcip.pl

MARCIN (POL)	1968	115	25,46		2,50	800	
STANISŁAW (POL)	1957	131	28,55	6,53		400	5.5
STEFAN (POL)	1964	132	28,76	6,53	2,60	400	5.5
ZBIGNIEW (POL)	1958	131	28,55	6,51	2,40	400	5.5

Dredging support and marine services around Poland

PROJECT ŻEGLUGA SP Z.O.O.

ul Piotra Skargi 19, 71-423 Szczecin, Poland
Tel : +48 91 43 00 470   Fax : +48 91 43 00 490
E-mail : mail@projectzegluga.pl
Website : www.projectzegluga.pl

RAFAL (POL)		79	21,08	6,10	2,20	400	6.0
SERWAL (POL)	1969	115	25,34	6,28	3,70	800	12.0
SERWAL 2 (POL)	1972	243	29,96	8,80	4,25	2800	30.0
(ex Multratug 11-03; Mercur-00)							
SERWAL 3 (POL)	1962	112	29,87	6,62	4,15	1370	18.5
(ex Multratug 14-03; Petronella J. Goedkoop-03)							

Towage services at the ports of Szczecin and Police and on the Szczecin-Świnoujście waterway

JAN STEPNIEWSKI S-KA

ul Legionowa 62/4, 81-413 Gdynia, Poland
Tel : +48 58 620 7102   Fax : +48 58 621 8421
E-mail : info@seatowage.com.pl
Website : www.seatowage.com.pl
Livery - Black hull, red housing, white wheelhouse; white funnel bearing JS monogram.

IKAR (POL) (ex Craigdarrah-94)	1966	171	29,98	7,98	2,92	1200	16.0
IRBIS (POL) (ex Kemsing-93)	1960	134	28,22	7,60	3,12	1000	14.5
JAGUAR (POL) (ex Wandelaar-04)	1971	280	32,98	8,70	3,50	2000	28.0
LEOPARD (SVK)	1969	269	33,33			1650	20.0

Coastal towage around Europe

Once again Europoort is the background but on this occasion it is the IKAR which passes inward bound and heading for Rotterdam on 26 January 2005.

(Dominic McCall)

STOCZNIA GDYNIA

ul Czechosłowacka 3, 81-969 Gdynia, Poland
Tel : +48 58 621 0879   Fax : +48 58 621 0789
E-mail : mm@stocznia.gdynia.pl
Website : www.stocznia.gdynia.pl

HELIOS (POL)	1975	113	25,68	6,81		935
OKEANOS (POL)	1977	113	25,68	6,81		935

Towage services at Gdynia

SZCZECIN-SWINOUJSCIE PORT AUTHORITY (ZARZĄD PORTU SZCZECIN-ŚWINOUJŚCIE SA)

ul Bytomska 7, 70-603 Szczecin, Poland
Tel : +48 91 430 8240   Fax : +48 91 462 4842
Website : www.port.szczecin.pl

ARION (POL)	1982	330	35,72	9,36	4,18	2500	30.0
ARMON (POL)	1982	330	35,00	9,40	3,52	2500	30.0
CYKLOP (POL)	1966	186	28,50	8,41	3,25	1650	
GLADIATOR (POL)	1976	177	29,39	8,31	3,09	1200	
GOLIAT (POL)	1965	227	31,70	8,40	3,60	1500	
HERMES (POL)	1975	184	29,29	8,31	3,80	1200	
KUGUAR (POL)	1970	115	25,48	6,84	2,70	800	

There is still plenty of evidence of winter in this view of the KUGUAR at Szczecin on 4 March 2001.

(Barry Standerline)

MOCNY (POL)	1974	177	29,32	8,31	3,08	1200
NIEDŹWEIDŹ (POL)	1967	119	25,46	6,84	2,50	800
*STRAŻAK-22 (POL)	1965	112	32,16	5,92	1,73	540
*STRAŻAK-25 (POL)	1978	276	37,34	9,22	3,60	2700
ZEUS (POL)	1966	186	28,43	8,41	3,25	1650

Towage services at Szczecin-Świnoujście and in the Baltic
* Dedicated fire-fighting vessels

SZCZECIŃSKA STOCZNIA REMONTOWA "GRYFIA"
ul Ludowa 13, 71-700 Szczecin, Poland
Tel : +48 91 422 4451   Fax : +48 91 424 23319
E-mail : gryfia@gryfia.com.pl
Website : www.gryfia.com.pl

LEOPARD (POL)	1967	119	25,46	6,81	2,50	800
TYGRYS (POL)	1966	119	25,51	6,81	2,50	800

Towage services at the Gryfia shipyard in Szczecin

'WUŻ' PORT & MARITIME SERVICES

ul Przemysłowa 4, Nowy Port, Gdańsk 80-542, Poland
Tel : +48 58 343 6540   Fax : +48 58 343 0534
E-mail : wuz@portgdansk.pl
Website : www.wuz.portgdansk.pl
Livery - Orange hull and housing with white wheelhouse; orange funnel with company emblem

AGIS (POL)	1981	336	35,67	9,38	4,02	2500	30.0
AJAKS (POL)	1974	336	35,34	9,38	3,84	2500	30.0
ARES (POL)	1976	336	35,67	9,38	3,86	2500	30.0
ARGO (POL)	1981	331	35,67	9,38	4,11	2500	30.0
ATLAS II (POL)	1966	186	28,56	8,00	4,20	1650	22.5
BÓBR (POL)	1975	111	24,20	6,95	2,24	900	10.5
HERCULES II (POL)	1966	186	28,58	8,00	4,20	1650	22.5
MIŚ (POL)	1969	111	25,46	6,79	2,69	800	12.0
SŁON (POL)	1975	111	24,20	6,95	2,24	900	10.5
TAURUS (POL)	2001	250	30,00	10,50	5,35	3300	42.0
TYTAN (POL)	1995	307	29,76	9,00	5,08	3890	47.0
ŻBIK (POL)	1975	184	29,30	8,31	3,08	1200	17.0

Towage services at Gdańsk

The sun is just beginning to set at the end of a warm summer day and highlights the AGIS at Gdansk on 6 August 2003.

(Dominic McCall)

'WUŻ' SHIPPING & PORT SERVICES GDYNIA COMPANY LTD

Polska 1, Pl-81-339 Gdynia, Poland
Tel : +48 58 627 4394   Fax : +48 621 5133
E-mail : wuz@port.gdynia.pl
Website : www.port.gdynia.pl/a_wuz.php

HEKTOR (POL)	1982	113	23,44	6,81	3,80	900	14.0
HERAKLES (POL)	1966	183	26,52	8,00	4,00	1650	22.5
HEROS (POL)	1998	365	30,23	9,80	3,80	4000	45.0
KRONOS (POL)	1966	181	26,59	8,00	4,00	1650	22.5
MARS (POL)	1977	179	25,02	8,00	4,00	1200	17.0
MOCARZ (POL)	1978	113	23,51	6,81	3,80	900	14.0
ODYS (POL)	1979	329	35,63	9,36	4,90	2500	34.0
ODYSEUSZ (POL)	1980	329	35,63	9,36	4,90	2500	34.0

Towage services at Gdynia

Another sunny day in Poland finds the MARS at work at Gdynia. The date was 28 July 2002.

(Dominic McCall)

ZAKLAD USŁUG ŻEGLUGOWYCH SP. Z O.O.

ul Ludowa 16, 71-700 Szczecin, Poland
Tel : +48 91 434 77 00   Fax : +48 91 434 77 00

TRYTON (POL)	2002	360	30,00	9,85	4,20	4000	50.0
(ex Dhoce-04)							
WULKAN (POL)	1976	177	29,37	8,31	3,09	1200	

Towage services at Szczecin

TUGS - SWEDEN

BLOMS BOGSERTJÄNST AB
Uno Blom, Vallmostigen 9, 664 32 Grums, Sweden
Tel/Fax : +46 55 51 04 44
E-mail : info@blomsbogsertjanst.se
Website : www.blomsbogsertjanst.se

HJALMAR (SWE)			12,40	3,80	1,60	230	5.0
THOR av GRUMS (SWE)	1954	130	24,50	6,91	3,90	1000	12.0

(ex Thor-96; Garpen-93)

EDBERGS REDERI
Box 1640, 751 46 Uppsala, Sweden
Tel : +34 70 74 04 733
E-mail : edbergsrederi@email.com

HERVOR (SWE)	1915	26	16,32	4,29	1,80

GÄVLE BOGSERING OCH SJOENTREPRENAD AB
P.O. Box 2084, 194 02 Upplands-Vasby, Sweden
Managed for AB Sylen (Sweden)

KARL ALFRED (SWE)	1902	150	31,34		3,20	1120

(ex Karl-Manfred af Gryt-96; Doggen-91; Ellwe-56; Doggen-19;
Director Louis Gutjahar VI-17)

Certainly not looking more than a hundred years old, the KARL ALFRED is seen at Gävle on 22 July 2004.

(Bernard McCall)

GUTE BOGSER OG MARIN SERVICE AB

Valleviken, S-620 34 Lärbro, Sweden
Tel : +46 498 22 30 00   Fax : +46 498 22 32
E-mail : gutetug@valleviken.com
Website : www.miljoisolering.com/gutetug

HARDING (SWE)	1918/85	187	27,70	6,82	3,60	1000	12.0
(ex Ramö-80; Renö-77; Sökaren-59)							
VEGA (SWE)	1964/79	458	43,58	9,80	3,70	1999	19.0

Towage and marine services on Gotland

The HARDING is seen at Visby, the main port on the island of Gotland.

(Alastair Paterson)

HALMSTADS HAMN & STUVERI AB

P.O. Box 1, 301 02 Halmstad, Sweden
Tel : +46 35 155300   Fax : +46 35 170593
E-mail : bogserab@telia.com

STIG (SWE)	1967	217	29,52	9,00	3,81	2459
(ex Harald-94; Uttern-69)						

Towage services at Halmstad

HELSINGBORG BOGSER AB

Box 821, S-251 08 Helsingborg, Sweden
Tel : +46 42 106 322   Fax : +46 42 135 483
E-mail : christer.friberg@port.helsingborg.se
Website : www.port.helsingborg.se/swedish.bogser

DUNKER (SWE)	1988	297	30,00	10,03	4,65	3600	44.0
KULLEN (SWE)	1976	228	27,50	8,10	3,95	2640	30.0

Towage services at Helsingborg

The PAMPUS catches the last rays of the setting sun at Kalmar in August 2002.

(Bernard McCall)

KALMAR HAMNFÖRVALTNING

P.O. Box 810, S-391 28 Kalmar, Sweden
Tel : +46 480 56 200

PAMPUS (SWE)	1958	185	28,78	8,06	4,20	1200	14.0

Towage services at Kalmar

KARLSHAMNS HAMN OCH STUVERI AB

P.O. Box 8, SE-374 21 Karlshamn, Stillerydshamnen, Sweden
Tel : +46 454 30 50 00   Fax : +46 454 30 50 30
E-mail : info@karlshamshamn.se
Website : www.karlshamnshamn.se

HARRY STONE (SWE)	1975	132	24,39	8,18	3,80	1360	
KARLSHAMN (SWE)	1980	194	26,90	8,50	3,80	2000	26.0

(ex Aros-03; Aros To-96)

Towage services at Karlshamn

REDERI KRAFT AB

3 Hollandareveien, Kalmar, Sweden

KRAFT (SWE)	1956	117	24,50	7,07	3,60	1200	13.0

(ex Hallsta II-96; Voima-82; Birger-79; Bjornen-73; Per-69)

RENÖ (SWE)	1958	199	29,01	8,31	3,80	2000	

(ex Erik-79; Obbola-78; Holmsund-68)

ROLF KENNETH LINDBERG

P.O. Box 47, 130 25 Ingmarso, Sweden

MONS (SWE)	1963	139	27,28	7,85	3,21	900

(ex Bob-96; Mons-96; Bob-86; Sjösport-86; Bob-85)

LULEÅ BOGSERBÅTS AB

Strömörvägen 9, 974 37 Luleå, Sweden
Tel : +46 920 29 30 00   Fax : +46 920 29 40 27
E-mail : bogserbat@lulea.se
Website : www.lulea.se
Livery - Red hull, cream housing and wheelhouse; red funnel with company logo

VALKYRIA (SWE)	1977	312	32,28	9,72	5,20	3520	35.0
VICTORIA (SWE)	1979	239	27,20	9,69	4,65	2640	25.0
(ex Veronica-82)							
VISCARIA (SWE)	2000	603	35,75	12,28	6,20	6120	62.0

Towage services at Luleå

The three tugs at Luleå await their next duty at their home port on 24 July 2004. The VICTORIA is nearest to the camera and VALKYRIA astern of her. The VISCARIA lies at the other side of the jetty.

(Bernard McCall)

MACROCE RYDIN AB

P.O. Box 24155, 10451 Stockholm, Sweden
Tel : +46 783 18 25   Fax : +46 660 11 22

DRAGA (SWE)	1917	113	25,15	6,76	3,96	510

(ex Oaxen Beta-64; Bolinders IV-34)

MARIN & HAVERIKONSULT KA AB
Fjällgatan 34, 116 28 Stockholm, Sweden
Tel : +358 8 714 94 50   Fax : +358 8 702 21 82
E-mail : info@tug.se
Website : www.tug.se

TED (SWE)	1961	153	26,52	7,65	3,65	1415	15.0
(ex Retu-99; Ted-96)							
TOM (SWE)	1968		16,80	5,42		400	
(ex Lillö-03)							
TUG (SWE)	1974	176	26,62	8,84	2,80	2400	

(ex Merchantman-01; Nore Commander-00; Balt 2-99; Bugsier 5-99)
Also the small tug LEIF
Towage and marine services at Stockholm

MODO PAPER AB
P.O. Box 1314, 111 83 Stockholm, Sweden

KÄMPE (SWE)	1977	296	29,62	9,00	4,26	2640	25.0

(ex Kempe-77)
Towage and marine services at Husum

The quaysides of many Scandinavian ports are dominated by huge industrial complexes, often connected with the forest products industries. The KÄMPE is dwarfed by a section of the pulp and paper mill at Husum in the north-east of Sweden. The date is 23 July 2004.

(Bernard McCall)

MÄLARHAMNAR AB
Västerås- Seglargatan 3, 721 32 Västerås, Sweden
Tel : +46 21 15 01 00, Fax : +46 21 15 01 40
E-mail : port@malarhamnar.se
Website : www.malarhamnar.se

ATHOS (SWE)	1960	184	28,00	8,02	3,65
(ex Agö-82; Frej-73)					
BORE af VÄSTERÅS (SWE)	1962	155	26,80	7,98	3,60
(ex Bore-80)					

Towage services at Västerås and Köping

NORTH CONTRACTOR AB
Tel : 46 76 223 8319
E-mail : northcontractors@home.se

RAN (SWE)	1953	97	23,42	6,22	2,70	665	8.0
(ex Brommo)							

NOÅS NORDMUDDRING AB
P.O. Box 47, 891 21 Örnsköldsvik, Sweden
Tel : +46 660 37 05 75   Fax : +46 660 37 06 30
E-mail : noas@telia.com
Website : www.noasnordmuddring.se

FRANS MICHAEL (SWE)	1917	212	31,42	8,18	4,40		
JÄRVEN (SWE)	1973	251	30,83	8,84	4,10	2100	20.0

Towage services at Örnsköldsvik and Gävle

The JÄRVEN at Gävle on 22 July 2004.

(Bernard McCall)

NORDIC STEAMER LTD
Strömstad
ISBJÖRN (SWE)   1958   152   26,01   7,80   3,64   1260   15.0
(ex Sjoakraft-04; Avantus-01; Jäverön-98; Isbjörn-87)

NORRLANDS SJÖENTREPRENAD
Skeppsbron 31, 871 30 Härnösand, Sweden
Tel/Fax : +46 611 207 77
E-mail : torbjorn@nse.nu
Website-www.nse.nu
MAX (SWE)   1969   70   21,35   6,50   3,30   720   10.0
Towage and marine services at Härnösand

NORRSUNDET BRUKS AB
P.O. Box 4, 817 01 Norrsundet, Sweden
STARKODDER (SWE)   1953   197   29,72   8,13   4,29   1020
Towage services at Norrsundet

OXELÖSUND HAMN AB
Box 1200, SE-613 24 Oxelösund, Sweden
Tel : + 46 155 25 80 00
E-mail : oxelosunds.hamn@oxhamn.se
Website : www.oxham.se
SIMSON
av OXELÖSUND (SWE) 1976   181   25,53   8,92   3,90   2870   28.0
(ex Stig-94)
Towage and icebreaking duties at Oxelösund

On 15 August 1998, the SIMSON lies at Oxelösund along with the ARCTIC HELIOS and AXEL of the Röda Bolaget fleet.

(Bernard McCall)

RÖDA BOLAGET AB

PO Box 108, Ostra Hamngatan 5, S-401 21 Gothenburg, Sweden
Tel : +46 31 10 97 00   Fax : +46 31 11 25 64
E-mail : info@rodabolaget.se
Website : www.svitzerwijsmuller.com

ARCTIC HELIOS (SWE)	1973	304	32,90	9,50	4,33	3155	35.0
(ex Helios-85; Victoria-81)							
BJÖRN							
af GÖTEBORG (SWE)	1992	356	32,90	10,00	3,40	4000	53.0
BOHUS (SWE)	1974	353	33,13	9,76	5,13	3900	40.0
BONDEN (SWE)	1974	349	33,13	9,76	5,13	3900	38.0
BOSS (SWE)	1995	496	36,24	12,22	5,20	5460	57.0
FREJA (SWE)	1999	453	33,65	11,25	5,12	4900	64.0
GÖSTA (SWE)	1968	216	29,52	9,00	3,89	2500	23.0
KNUT (SWE)	1976	179	25,00	8,92	3,88	2820	28.0
(ex Javeron-01; Viscaria-00; Knut-93)							
LARS (SWE)	1992	356	32,90	10,00	3,40	4000	53.0
PER (SWE)	1972	330	32,78	9,50	4,85	3410	33.0
ST. OLOF (SWE)	1974	309	32,50	9,50	4,85	3400	33.0
(ex Kristian-86)							
STORVIK (SWE)	1962	62	19,02	5,70	3,00	680	6.5
VIKTOR (SWE)	1966	101	22,26	7,11	4,20	870	8.5
(ex Boy-87; Tor-84)							

Towage service at various Swedish ports
Part of the Svitzer-Wijsmuller Group

The ST OLOF and KNUT at Norrköping in July 2002.

(Bernard McCall)

ROSLAGS BOGSER AB

Skogsv. 8, 763 35 Hallstavik, Sweden
Tel : +46 17 52 04 28   Fax; +46 17 52 01 40

FRIGGA (SWE)	1967	186	29,21	8,06	2,99	1750	18.0

Towage services at Hallstavik

RUNDVIKS BOGSERBÅT AB

Fjärdängsvägen 2, 914 41 Rundvik, Sweden
Tel : +46 930 305 46   Fax : +46 930 309 75
E-mail : info@rundviksrederi.se
Website : www.rundviksrederi.se

AXEL af RUNDVIK (SWE)	1967	218	29,52	9,00	4,04	2460	25.0

(ex Axel af Göteborg-01, Axel av Halmstad-92, Axel-89)

BÅDAN (SWE)	1963	332	36,89	9,61	4,20	1260	15.0

(ex Naantali-92)
Towage services at Rundvik

SANDINGE BOGSERING & SJÖTRANSPORT (SBS)

Skal Hedarna 166, 453 92 Lysekil, Sweden
Tel : +46 523 6607 45   Fax : +46 523 6607 22
E-mail : info@sandinge.com
Website : www.sandinge.com

ALPO (SWE)	1977		6,66	2,70	1,60	110	
BO (SWE)	1957		8,40	2,10	0,70	127	
BUTTRIX (SWE)	1959		5,30	2,60	1,00	35	
DUNNERVATTNET (SWE)	1956		6,00	2,25	0,50	40	
HAKA (SWE)	1986		7,10	3,00	1,50	209	1.9
HECTOR (SWE)	1979		11,65	4,45	1,80	314	4.0
HJALMAR (SWE)	1973		9,00	2,50	1,30	87	1.0
KAJ (SWE)	1975		5,62	2,70	1,50	110	
KALLE (SWE)	1965		10,34	2,80	1,75	148	
LILL-PÄR (SWE)	1979		7,10	3,00	1,50	106	1.3
LUTO (SWE)	1981	24	12,63	4,69	1,85	234	4.0
PETTER (SWE)	1962		10,15	3,20	1,70	141	
PILEN (SWE)	1960		6,95	2,10	0,80	12	
RYGENE (SWE)	1978	35	17,60	4,81	2,00	560	7.5
SEPPO (SWE)	1980		10,25	3,40	1,20	300	2.5
SIXTEN (SWE)	1961		8,40	2,10	0,70	127	
SORVA (SWE)	1974		12,00	3,70	1,45	231	
TAIMEN (SWE)	1962		10,11	3,09	1,70	122	
TIMO (SWE)	1977		7,10	2,70	1,60	87	
TRIODEN (SWE)	1968		7,60	2,90	1,30	80	
ÅKE (SWE)	1909		11,50	3,30	1,80	150	

Icebreaking, towage and barge services at Lysekil, Gothenburg, Uddevalla and Skoghall

SKELLEFTEÅ HAMN

Järnvägsleden 81, SE-932 00 Skelleftehamn, Sweden
Tel : +46 910 331 30   Fax : +46 344 38
AITIK   (SWE)   1968   264   31,17   9,28   4,11   2440
Towage services at Skelleftehamn

SKÄRNÄS TERMINAL AB

Box 15, SE-825 21, Iggesund, Sweden
Tel : +46 650 280 00   Fax : +46 650 283 74
E-mail : postmaster@skarnas-terminal.se
Website-www.skarnas-terminal.se
DE GEER   (SWE)   1964   239   30,05   8,64   4,60   1680
Towage services at Skarnas

SMÅLANDSHAMNAR AB

Norra Strandgatan 50, 572 32 Oskarshamn, Sweden
Te: +46 491 872 00   Fax; +46 491 163 22
E-mail : info@port.oskarshamn.se
Website : www.port.oskarshamn.se
HERBERT   (SWE)   1976   181   25,53   8,92   3,90   2850   28.5
(ex Hans-91)
LARS
    af OSKARSHAMN   (SWE) 1965   143   24,62   7,73   3,64   1100   15.0
(ex Hero-99)
Towage services at Oskarshamn

SUNDSVALLS HAMN AB

Box 805, S-851 23 Sundsvall, Sweden
Tel : +46 60 12 31 80   Fax : +46 60 19 35 07
E-mail : info@sundsvallshamn.se
Website : www.sundsvallshamn.se
BULL   (SWE)   1972   271   32,15   9,02   4,80   2500
Towage and icebreaking services at Sundsvall

SWEDISH MARITIME ADMINISTRATION

SE-601 78 Norrköping, Sweden
Tel : +46 11 19 10 00   Fax : +46 11 19 14 00
E-mail : hk@sjofartsverket.se
Managed for Svenskt Isbrytarkonsortium (Sweden)
ODEN   (SWE)   1989   9438   107,80 25,00   8,50   21739   150.0
Icebreaking duties around Swedish coast

SÖDERHAMNS STUVERI & HAMN AB

Box 5082, 826 05 Söderhamn, Sweden
Tel : +46 270 28 41 32   Fax : +46 270 28 41 26
E-mail : sshab@telia.com
GIBB   (SWE)   1962   257   30,03   8,84   1650
Towage services at Söderhamn

SÖLVESBORGS SKEPPSMÄKLERI & SPENDITIONSKONTOR AB

294 35 Sölvesborg, Sweden
Tel : +46 456 422 55   Fax : +46 456 130 83
E-mail : info@solvesborgskeppsmakleri.se
Website : www.solvesborgskeppsmakleri.se
HAFNIA   (SWE)   1955   91   23,67   6,20   3,30   665   7.0
(ex Hardig)
Towage and icebreaking services at Sölvesborg

TIMRÅ BOGSERING OCH BÄRGNING AB

Box 32, 860 30 Sörberge, Sweden
Tel : +46 60 57 96 44
J. A. ENHÖRNING   (SWE)   1961   17,00   5,50   3,00   700
(ex Troilö)
Harbour towage in the Sundsvall area and coastal towage

The J. A. ENHÖRNING at Fagervik on 23 July 2004.

(Bernard McCall)

UMEÅ HAMN AB

Postfack 83, 913 22 Holmsund, Sweden
Tel : +46 90 16 32 80   Fax : +46 90 243 06
E-mail : umeahamn@umea.se
Website : www.umeahamn.se

KRONÖ (SWE)	1970	368	34,57	9,22	5,00	2600

Towage services at Umeå

VÄNERHAMN AB

Huvudkontor, Stuvargatan 1, 652 21 Karlstad, Sweden
Tel : +46-54-14 48 60   Fax : +46 54 21 33 16
E-mail : vanerhamn@vanerhamn.se
Website : www.vanerhamn.se

KARL af KARLSTAD (SWE)	1965	253	32,31	9,02	4,29	3020	26.0
(ex Karl-00)							
LIDKÖPING (SWE)	1967	89	23,30	6,70	3,30	920	9.0

Towage and ice breaking services at Karlstad and other ports on Lake Vänern

ÅDALENS STUVERI AB

Drottninggatan 4, 872 30 Kramfors, Sweden
Tel : +46 612 131 20   Fax : +46 612 123 27
E-mail : info@adalens-stuveri.se
Website : www.adalens-stuveri.se

JOHN EKMAN (SWE)	1961	218	29,60	8,36	3,90	1200	12.0

Towage and icebreaking duties on the Ångermanälven

ÖSTERSTRÖMS REDERI AB

P.O. Box 44, SE-601 02 Norrköping, Sweden
Tel : +46 11 19 62 00   Fax : +46 11 19 62 39
E-mail : osterstroms@osterstroms.se
Website : www.osterstroms.se

KARL-ERIK (SWE)	1975	324	32,82	10,06	4,15	2818	
(ex Hector-90)							
MEGA (SWE)	1975/93	768	39,90	12,90	5,10	5245	n/a
(ex Aatos-93, Teuvo-85)							

Pusher services handling the company's barges around the Baltic

UNKNOWN OWNERS

SWEDJEHOLM (SWE)	1956	120	24,52	7,42	3,65	1060

(ex Karl-Manfred-94; Ran av Vaddo-82; Illern-79; Thetis-62)

INDEX OF VESSEL NAMES

Current names are in CAPITAL letters; previous names are in lower case.

Name	No.	Name	No.	Name	No.	Name	No.
CAT-1	33	ENØ	40	Federal Atlantic	17	HAKA	103
Cement 8	77	Eol	37	FELIX	85	Halla V	65
Cement 9	54	ERIDAN	49	FENJA	44	HALLI	51
Challenger III	14	Erik	97	FENNICA	5	Hallsta II	97
CHANKO	81	Ernst	70	Finn	52	Halvard	32
Chatina	7	ESBJERG 1	34	Flexservice 2	12	HAMLET	55
Cheng Chau	82	ESKO	53	Flodsprutan	60	HANHI	58
CHIEF	83	Esta	62	FOBOS	68	Hans	104
Chignecto Bay	14	ESVAGT BRAVO	7	Formidable	43	Hans Oscar	57
CHR. KONTTURI	61	ESVAGT CAPELLA	7	Forte	78	Hans Oskar	57
CIKLONS	67	ESVAGT CHARLIE	7	Forties Moon	74	HARALD	55
Cinhco	82	Esvagt Charlie	7	FOX	85	Harald	96
Clausentum	43	ESVAGT CONNECTOR	7	FRAM	55	Hardig	105
Coburg	76	Esvagt Connector	7	FRANK	38	HARDING	96
Columbus	86	ESVAGT CORONA	7	FRANS MICHAEL	100	Hargo	34
Courageux	71	ESVAGT DELTA	7	Fredrikstad	78	HARRY STONE	97
Craigdarrah	91	Esvagt Delta	7	Fredsgrogg	59	HARSTAD	21
CYKLOP	92	ESVAGT ECHO	7	FREJ	60	Harta	32
		ESVAGT GAMMA	7	Frej	100	Havila Borgstein	3
Dagmar	39	ESVAGT KAPPA	7	FREJA	102	Havila Charisma	3
DANASUND	43	ESVAGT OBSERVER	7,8	FRIGGA (1967)	103	Havila Charmer	3
Darsser Ort	41	ESVAGT OMEGA	7	FRIGGA (1998)	44	Havila Chieftain	3
DE GEER	104	ESVAGT PRESERVER	7	Frode	82	HAVILA CLEVER	12
Director Louis Gutjahar IV	95	ESVAGT PREVENTER	7	Fru Olsen	83	Havila Crown	4
DIVER MASTER	32	ESVAGT PROMOTOR	7			Havila Eko	4
DMS Condor	34	ESVAGT PROTECTOR	7	Gabarus Bay	15	HAVILA FAITH	12
Doggen	95	ESVAGT SIGMA	7	Galati 1	67	HAVILA FAME	12
Dolphin	65	EUROSUND	43	Galati 2	67	HAVILA FAVOUR	12
Donn Hugin	18			GARM	44	HAVILA FORCE	12
Donn Myre	19	FADER'N	78	Garpen	95	HAVILA FORTRESS	12
Dorum	34	Fairplay II	32	Gaven	55	HAVILA FORTUNE	12
Dox	52	Fairplay VII	32	GECO SCORPIO	21	HAVILA HARMONY	12
DRAGA	98	FANCY	63	Geeste	82	Havila Hidra	4
Duchray	75	FAR CENTURION	8	Geo Boy	19	Havila Lista	3
Duga	81	FAR CRUSADER	8	Geraki	49	HAVILA RUNDE	12
Duncurlew	75	FAR FOSNA	8	Gerd Viking	18	Havila Scotia	4
DUNKER	96	FAR GRIMSHADER	8	Gerda Grenius	7	HAVILA SEA	12
DUNNERVATTNET	103	FAR GRIP	8	Gerjo	37	HAVILA SEARCHER	12
DUX	85	FAR SAGA	8	GIBB	105	HAVILA SKY	13
Dux	41	FAR SAILOR	8	GINTARAS	70	HAVILA STAR	13
Dynan	45	FAR SALTIRE	8	GLADIATOR	92	HAVILA SUN	13
DZINTAURS	67	FAR SANTANA	8	GOLIAT	92	Havila Surf	4
		FAR SCANDIA	8	Goliath	39	Havila Tampen	4
E. L. Preston	48	Far Scandia	8	Goliath Carl (1977)	44	HAVILA TERN	13
Echo Star	24	FAR SCOTIA	8	Goliath Carl (1980)	44	HAVILA TIGRIS	13
Edda Atlantic	12	Far Scotia	4	Goliath Fur (1908)	37	HAVILA TROLL	13
EDDA FJORD	31	FAR SCOUT	8,9	Goliath Fur (1975)	39	HAVKATTEN III	36
EDDA FONN	31	Far Scout	5	Goliath Gol	48	Havsvind	7
EDDA FRAM	31	FAR SEA	10	Goliath Røn	44	HAVSØY	79
EDDA FRENDE	31	Far Searcher	12	Goliath Thy	37	HECTOR (1975)	55
EDDA FREYA	31	FAR SENIOR	9	Goliath I	44	HECTOR (1979)	103
EDDA FRIGG	31	FAR SERVER	9	Goliath IV	45	Hector	106
Edda Sea	12	FAR SERVICE	9	Goliath V	40	Heimo Saarinen	55
Edda Sprite	12	FAR SKY	10	Gorm	34	HEKTOR	94
Edda Star	24	Far Sky	22	Gos 1	19	HELENE C	38
Eft	42	FAR SLEIPNER	9	Grampian Osprey	19	HELIOS (1975)	91
Efta	42	FAR SOUND	9	Grane (1951)	40	HELIOS (1976)	55
EGIL	44	FAR SOVEREIGN	9	Grane (1977)	39	Helios	102
Eide Chief	80	Far Spirit	22	Grane III	39	Hellesund	19
EIDE FOX	75	FAR SPLENDOUR	9	GREVEN	72	Helmer	40
EIDE MAX	75	FAR STAR	9	Grip	19	HENRIC	53
EIDE REX	75	FAR STRAIT	9	GRZEGORZ	87	Henric (1958)	54
Eide Rex	80	FAR STREAM	9	Gullbas	27	Henric (1969)	53
EIDE TRAVELER	75	FAR STRIDER	9	GYLTINGEN	74	Henriette	7
EIK	80	FAR SUPERIOR	9	GÖSTA	102	Hepa	52
Eikvaag	39	FAR SUPPLIER	9	GÖTA	60	HERA	86
Einar Senior	74	Far Supplier	11			HERAKLES	94
Eir	56	FAR SUPPORTER	9	H. KANTER	49	Herbert	55
Ellen III	36	FAR SWIFT	9	H3	62	HERBERT (1966)	82
Ellwe	95	FAR SWORD	9	Haabas	84	HERBERT (1976)	104
Else Wejse	37	FAR SYMPHONY	9	Haabrand	82	HERCULES (1960 54grt)	65
Emerald Bas	12	FAR VISCOUNT	9	HAABULL	74	HERCULES (1960, 161grt)	63
Emerald Sprite	12	Faroe Connector	7	Haahr Trumf	34	HERCULES (1966)	82
Emil	51	FART	55	Hadarvåg	79	HERCULES II	93
ENGLISHMAN	88	FARØY	76	HAFNIA	105	Herman Kubbe	57

Melløs II 71
Menes 19
MERCHANTMAN 75
Merchantman 99
Mercur (1964) 76
Mercur (1972) 90
Mercurius 52
MERIKARHU 61
Merkuriy 68
Mester 33
METEOR 63
Meteor 63
Michael I 83
Middlebank 7
Mikal I 74
MIMER 44
Mimer (1956) 79
Mimer (1959) 33
Mimer (1975) 39
MINI MAMMUT 84
MINOS 63
MINOTAUR 90
MIŚ 93
Mjølner 48
MJØLNER (2001) 81
MJØLNER (2002) 77
MOCARZ 94
MOCNY 92
Mona Viking 28
Monica 32
Monika Viking 28
MONS 98
Mons 98
Montenovo 44
MONTU 50
Mor 76
Moresby 24
Motorman 75
MULTI MAMMUT 84
MUSONS 67
Multratug 11 90
Multratug 14 90
Musson 67
Myre Seadiver 19
MÆRDO 79
MÆRSK ACHIEVER 16
MÆRSK ASSISTER 16
Mærsk Assister 10
MÆRSK ATTENDER 16
Mærsk Attender 10
MÆRSK BATTLER 16
MÆRSK BLAZER 16
MÆRSK BOULDER 16
MÆRSK CHAMPION 16
MÆRSK CHIEFTAIN 16
MÆRSK CLIPPER 16
MÆRSK FEEDER 16
MÆRSK FETCHER 16
MÆRSK FIGHTER 16
MÆRSK FORWARDER 16
MÆRSK FRONTIER 16
MÆRSK LAUNCHER 16
MÆRSK LEADER 16
MÆRSK LIFTER 16
MÆRSK MASTER 16
MÆRSK PACER 16
MÆRSK PROMOTER 17
MÆRSK PROVIDER 17
MÆRSK PUNCHER 17
MÆRSK SEEKER 17
MÆRSK SUPPLIER 17
MÆRSK TACKLER 17
Mærsk Tackler 22
MÆRSK TERRIER 17
MÆRSK TOPPER 17

MÆRSK WINNER 17
Naantali 103
NAKSKOV HAVN II 39
Nalle 51
Namdalingen 81
NAMEJS 68
Nathurn 79
NAUTILUS MAMMUT 82
Navid 44
Navimer II 22
NEMO 51
NEPTUN 55
Neptun 68
Neris 70
NESBOY 74
Nesfoss 73
Nestor 76
Neuwerk 82
NICKE 63
NICO 62
NIEDŹWEIDŹ 92
NIEREN 35
NIKOLAJS NECIPORENKO 69
Nikolay Nechiporenko 69
Nils 42
Njord 53
No. 12 53
No. 13 61
No. 18 63
No. 20 86
Nor Truck 12
Nord 53
NORDBEVER 75
Norderney 79
NORDIC BRAVO 72
NORDICA 5
Nordmark 80
Nordryggen 72
Nore Commander 99
Norindo Sun 22
Normand 54
NORMAND ATLANTIC 24
NORMAND AURORA 24
NORMAND BORG 26
NORMAND CARRIER 24
NORMAND CUTTER 24
NORMAND DRAUPNE 24
NORMAND DROTT 24
NORMAND FLIPPER 24
NORMAND FLOWER 26
Normand Flower 22
NORMAND HUNTER 24
NORMAND IVAN 24,25
NORMAND JARL 25
NORMAND MARINER 26
NORMAND MASTER 26
NORMAND MERMAID 26
NORMAND MJOLNE 25
NORMAND NEPTUN 25
NORMAND PIONEER 25
NORMAND PRODUCE 25
Normand Produce 22
NORMAND PROGRESS 25
NORMAND PROSPER 25
NORMAND RANGER 25
NORMAND ROVER 26
NORMAND SKARVEN 25
NORMAND SKIPPER 25
NORMAND TITAN 25
NORMAND TRYM 25
NORMAND VESTER 26
NORSUND 43
North Breeze 13
NORTH CHALLENGER 11

NORTH CRUSADER 11
NORTH FORTUNE 11
North Fortune 11
NORTH MARINER 11
NORTH STREAM 11
NORTH TRAVELLER 11
NORTH TRUCK 11
NORTH VANGUARD 12
North-Sea Surveyor 19
Northern Admiral 5
NORTHERN CANYON 27
NORTHERN CHALLENGER 27
NORTHERN CHASER 27
NORTHERN CLIPPER 27
Northern Clipper 27
NORTHERN COMMANDER 27
Northern Commander 22
NORTHERN COMRADE 27
NORTHERN CORONA 27
NORTHERN CRUSADER 28
Northern Fortune 11
NORTHERN GAMBLER 27
NORTHERN GENESIS 27
NORTHERN MARINER 27
NORTHERN PRINCESS 28
NORTHERN QUEEN 28
NORTHERN RIVER 28
NORTHERN SUPPORTER 27
Northern Viking 22
NORTHERN WAVE 28

Oaxen Beta 98
Obbola 97
OCEAN CARRIER 22
Ocean Chief 80
OCEAN COMMANDER 22
OCEAN FIGHTER 22
OCEAN FLOWER 22
OCEAN KNARR 22
OCEAN LADY 80
OCEAN MAINPORT 22
Ocean Range 13
OCEAN SAFE 22
OCEAN SKY 22
OCEAN SPIRIT 22
OCEAN STAR 22
OCEAN VIKING 22
ODEN 104
ODIN 36
ODIN I 47,48
Odin II 36
ODIN II 48
Odin Safe 22
ODIN STEVNS 39
Odin Stevns 45
ODYS 94
ODYSEUSZ 94
Oil Challenger 14
Oil Champion 16
Oil Chancellor 14
Oil Chieftain 16
OKEANOS 91
OLAF 86
Ole Bakk 19
Ole Jacob 79
OLLI 63
OLSEN 78
OLYMPIC COMMANDER 20
Olympic Commander 22
OLYMPIC HERCULES 20
OLYMPIC ORION 20
OLYMPIC PEGASUS 20
OLYMPIC POSEIDON 20
OLYMPIC PRINCESS 20
OLYMPIC PROGRESS 20

OLYMPIC PROMOTER 20
OLYMPIC PROVIDER 20
OLYMPIC SUPPLIER 20
Omega 807 7
Orion (1974) 64
ORION (1974) 64
ORION (1986) 49
Orion Expeditor 64
ORJAKU 51
Oscar Tybring 36
OSKAR 72
Ost 60
OTSO 53
OTTO 63

Pacific Salvor 88
PALLAS 56
PAMPUS 97
Pampus 64
Pan Searcher 12
Pan Sky 22
Pankakoski II 61
Parainen 63
PARKKO 63
PASATS 67
PAX 85
PEETER 50
PEGASOS 57
Pellinki 63
PER 102
Per 97
Peresvet 50
Peter 74
PETRA 58
Petronella J. Goedkoop 90
PETTER 103
PILEN 103
Pionjar 86
Placentia Bay 15
Plan Searcher 12
PLUTO 56
Pluto 59
PLUTONS 68
PM 204 72
POLAR PEVEK 81
Polar Titan 25
Polarbris I 19
Polardyk 34
POLARIS 58
Polarnacht 19
Polarson 19
POLLUX 59
Pollux 7
PORIN KARHU 56
Porin Karhu 51
Porin Nalle 51
PORS 79
Portunus 73
POSEJDON 88
PRANGLI 49
Preserver 7
Preventer 7
PRIMUS 56
Promotor 7
PROTECTOR 56
Protector 7
Puuma 51

R 5 13
RAFAL 90
Rahja 60
RAJU 60
RALLAREN 72
Ramnes 33
Ramö 96

Name	No.	Name	No.	Name	No.	Name	No.
RAN	100	SASHA	24	SKANDI CARLA	6	Sterke	42
Ran av Vaddo	106	SATURN	49	SKANDI CHIEFTAIN	6	STEVNS	39
Randfonn	25	Saturn	68	SKANDI FALCON	6	Stevns (1968)	42
RAS	40	SAUKO	57	SKANDI FJORD	6	Stevns (1975)	44
Rau III	19	Scheibenhof	80	Skandi Fortune	11	STEVNS ARCTIC	39
Rauma I (1966)	63	Schelde	27	SKANDI FOULA	6	Stevns Bugser	44
Rauma I (1975)	48	Schepelsturm	88	SKANDI HAV	6	STEVNS GUARD	39
Rauma III (1968)	57	Sct Knud	33	Skandi Hawk	12	STEVNS ICEBIRD	40
Rauma III (1970)	62	Sea Guardian	28	SKANDI INSPECTOR	6	STEVNS MASTER	40
Rauma IV (1970)	57	Sea Pearl	10	SKANDI MARSTEIN	6	STEVNS OCEAN	40
Rauma IV (1978)	32	SEA REX	80	SKANDI MØGSTER	6	Stevns Tug	40
Rauni	40	Sea Truck	12	SKANDI NAVICA	6	STIG	96
RAUTARUUKI	52	Sea Worker	28	SKANDI PATAGONIA	6	Stig	101
Red Knight	86	Seaboard Castor	19	SKANDI PMS I	6	STINA	64
REM COMMANDER	21	SEABULK ASIA	12	SKANDI PMS II	6	Stirling Aquarius	18
REM FORTUNE	21	SEABULK		SKANDI RONA	6	Stirling Clyde	22
Rem Searcher	12	SOUTH ATLANTIC	26	SKANDI SOTRA	6	Stirling Forth	12
REM STADT	21	Seaforth Atlantic	17	SKANDI STOLMEN	6	Stirling Iona	12
REM SUPPLIER	21	Seaforth Centurion	8	SKANDI STORD	6	Stirling Pegasus	12
Rembakk	19	Seaforth Crusader	8	SKANDI TEXEL	6	Stirling Spey	12
Rembas	3	Seaforth Emperor	4	SKANDI WAVENEY	29	Stirling Tay	12
Rembertiturm	13	Seaforth Laird	7	SKANDI YARE	6	Stirling Tern	22
RENÖ	97	Seaforth Viscount	9	SKANSUND	43	Stockfors III	60
Renö	96	Sealion Columbia	22	SKAWLINK	42	STOKKÅS	79
Repola	63	Searcher	75	Skawlink	42	Stor Viking	63
Repola 4	57	Seaway Petrel	19	SKAWLINK III	42	Stor-Hacke	51
Repola 7	58	Selat Harima	44	SKILSØ	79	Stor-Joel	63
Rescue Eko	4	Selene	32	Sklinna	19	Storebirger	80
Rescue Kim	13	SEMBA	70	SKRUBBEN	78	STORESUND	43
Rescue Saga	12	Senorita	10	Skuld	40	Storfonn	16
Rescue Tern	13	SENTINEL	12	SKULD	44	Storgrogg (1939)	71
Retu	99	SEPPO	103	SLEIPNER (1981)	44	Storgrogg (1965)	59
REX	85	SERWAL	90	SLEIPNER (2002)	76	Stormcenter	41
Rex (1956)	79	SERWAL 2	90	SLON	93	Stormqueen	32
Rex (1962)	7	SERWAL 3	90	Smit-Lloyd Fame	12	STORVIK	102
Risøygutt	79	SEUT	83	Smit-Lloyd 92	7	Stout Truck	11
RISTO	60	Sever	69	Smit-Lloyd 115	75	Strathfoyle	43
Risto	54	Shelf Challenger	10	Smit-Lloyd 119	75	STRAŻAK-3	87
RITA SAJ	33	Shelf Ranger	10	Snik	63	STRAŻAK-5	87
Riverman	73	Shelf Supporter	10	SOFIE	24	STRAŻAK-11	87
Robbe	33	Shika	7	Sökaren	96	STRAŻAK-14	87
Roeggen	19	Shvituris	70	Solfonn	3	STRAŻAK-22	92
Rolf	79	SIDDIS MARINER	17	SOMERI	49	STRAŻAK-25	92
ROLLE	63	SIDDIS PILOT	17	SONTINJA	42	Stream Truck	11
ROLLO	40	SIDDIS SAILOR	17	Soru	69	STRIL CLIPPER	18
ROMBAK	72	SIDDIS SKIPPER	17,18	SORVA	103	STRIL MYSTER	18
RONDO	79	SIGGBAS	22,23	Sound Truck	11	STRIL NEPTUN	18
Ronnebeck	43	SIGYN	44	SOUNDLINK	42	STRIL ODIN	19
RÖNÖ	60	SILEX	85	Southern Jester	19	Stril Odin	22
Ronstad	19	SILVER STAR	24	SPARK	51	STRIL PIONEER	19
Rosscan Power	88	Sim	57	Spiekeroog	83	STRIL POSEIDON	19
ROTEVA	54	SIMSON	57,58	Sprite	12	Stril Poseidon	20
Roxo	82	Simson	57	SQUALUS	83	STRIL POWER	19
Royal	63	SIMSON av OXELÖSUND	101	ST OLOF	102	Stril Power	88
RUDOLF	49	Sira Girl	28	St Serf	33	STRIL SAFETY	19
Rudolf	49	Sira Odin	28	ST. 79	71	STRIL SUPPLIER	19
RUMB	47	SIRI	85	ST. 252	34	STRIL SUPPORTER	19
Rundik	32	SIRIUS	49	ST. 335	63	STRIL SURVEYOR	19
Runskär	71	Sirius	65	ST. 480	53	STRIL TENDER	19
RUSKEN	77	SIROKO	67	Stad Neptun	10	STRILBORG	19
Russo Balt	47	SISU	53	Stad Scandia	8	Strilborg	3
Rutane	7	SIXTEN	103	Stad Senja	11	STRILBRIS	19
RYGENE	103	Sjoakraft	101	Stad Sky	22	STRILFALK	19
RÖJVIK	65	Sjöbjörn	55	Stad Sleipner	9	STRILFISK	19
		Sjøbjørn	55	Stad Spirit	22	STRILHAUK	19
Salen II	42	Sjollen	58	Stad Supplier	22	STRILHAV	19
SAMI	51	Sjösport	98	STANISŁAW	90	STRILHVAL	19
SAMSON	90	Skafto	7	Star Aquarius	18	STRILMØY	19
Samson	79	SKANDI ADMIRAL	5	Star Pegasus	12	STRILODD	19
SANNE A	37	SKANDI BARRA	5	Starkgrogg	55	Striltral	19
Sar Castor	19	SKANDI BERGEN	5	STARKODDER	101	STRILVAKT	19
Sar Delta	19	SKANDI BETA	6	Staupfos	78	STRILVARD	19
SARTOR	22	SKANDI BUCHAN	5	STEEL	52,53	STRILØY	19
Sartor (1936)	19	SKANDI CALEDONIA	6	STEFAN	90	STUMBRAS	69,70
Sartor (1947)	19	SKANDI CAPTAIN	6	Stein	43	STYRBJORN	80

Name	No.	Name	No.	Name	No.	Name	No.
Styrbjorn	80	Thetis (1956)	106	TRYTON	94	VIKING NEREUS	6
Subriellen	7	Thetis (1961)	59	Tsiklon	67	VIKING POLAR	34
SUBSEA VIKING	6	THJOUR	65	TUG	99	VIKING POSEIDON	6
Suderøy	19	Thor (1904)	74	Tug	73	VIKING PRINCE	22
Suderøy V	19	Thor (1954)	95	Tug Frisøy	58	VIKING QUEEN	6
Suet	19	THOR (1904)	74	TUG MERCUR	76	VIKING SURF	7
Suffolk Mariner	27	THOR (1998)	35,36	TUG NESTOR	76	VIKING SWAN	29
Suffolk Supporter	28	THOR av GRUMS	95	TUGEV	47	VIKING THAUMAS	6
Sun Essex	37	THOR STEVNS	40	Tuggard	57	Viking Titan	25
Sun Supporter	22	Thor Stevns	38	Tunö	56	VIKING TROLL	6
Sun Tender	13	THOR III	74	TURSO	56	VIKTOR	102
Sunbas	13	THORAX	85	TUURA	61	Vimi	19
SURF VIKING	7	Thorvard	19	TYBRING	36	VISCARIA	98
SUSANNE A	37	THRAX	85	TYGRYS	92	Viscaria	102
SUSANNE SAJ	33	TID 1	61	TYR	56	VITUS	32
Suur Tyil	50	TID 41	57	Tyr (1956)	59	VIVAX	85
Svanö I	56	TID 49	62	Tyr (1959)	56	VLIELAND	46
SVARTA BJØRN	72	TID 169	54	Tyr (1981)	36	VOIKKAA	65
SVAVA	44	Tiger Boxer	56	Tyra	32	VOIMA	53
Svava (1962)	39	Tiger Orchid	82	Tyri	56	Voima (1919)	32
Svava (1980)	44	TIKKA	59	TYTAN	93	Voima (1939)	71
SVEASUND	43	TIMO	103			Voima (1956)	97
Sveasund	34	Tina A	42	UITTO 1	57	VOITTO	51
Svelviksand	80	Tina Pantos	7	UITTO 6	57	Volstad Senior	19
SVITZER APURE	34	TINTO	63	UKKO	53	VRANGSUND	78
SVITZER MARS	44	Tit	41	UKU	48	VULCANUS	73
SVITZER MENJA	45	Titan	79	ULLA	59	VØLUND	45
SVITZER MJØLNER	45	Toanui	17	Ulla Nord	7	Vølund	49
SVITZER MUNIN	45	TOFTE II	82	Ulla Somand	7		
SVYTURYS	70	TOLVAN	53	Uller	80	WAIJA	56
SWEDJEHOLM	106	TOM	99	URAN (2001)	89,90	Wandelaar	91
Sydfonn	14	Tom	50	URAN (2004)	50	Wargon	86
Symeri	49	TOM T	50	URD	45	WATERBJORN	79
SØLVBAS	22	Tond	18	Urd	39	WATERMAN	79
		Tonjer	19	Urho	52	Wegreto	74
TAIFUNS	67	Topdalsfjord II	80	URHU	53	West	54
TAIMEN	103	Tor (1904)	74	URSUS	41	West Penguin	12
TAK 1	71	Tor (1958)	56	Ursus	79	West Plover	22
TAK 2	70	Tor (1966)	102	Uttern	96	West Tern	13
TAK 3	70	TOR VIKING II	30			Westgarth	75
TAK 4	71	TORANES	81	Vaasa	60	WESTSUND	43
TAK 5	71	Torani	81	Vaksdal	81	Weswear	39
TAK 9	70	Torbas	3	VALKYRIA	98	Wih. Michaelsen	19
Takapu	17	Tordenskjold	73	VALKYRIEN	45	Wilanne	86
TAMBUR	83	Torefors	86	Varangis II	57	Wilhelm Hackman	32
TANDEM	69	Torian	73	Varnebank	56	Wilhelmina 8	86
TAPIO	54	Torna	60	Vastervik	80	WILK	87
Tapio	58	TORNATOR	60	VEGA	96	WULKAN	94
Tapio II	63	Tornator	60	VEGA I	48	Wäija	56
TARMO	61	Tornator IV	60	VELA	47		
Taru	59	Tornen	54	Veldig	35	Zacharias	12
TASUJA	50	Torrand	19	VELOX	85	ZBIGNIEW	90
Taucher O. Wulf 9	78	Torson	19	Velox	85	ŻBIK	93
TAURUS	93	TORVIK	56	VENE	47	ZEUS (1966)	92
Tawaki	17	Tott	75	VENTSPILS	68	ZEUS (1995)	56
Tayfun	67	Toy	32	Veronica	98	Zovushtchyi	78
Tebe	55	Tranevaag	79	Veronica Viking	22		
TED	99	Traust	83	VESTVERN	77	ÅKE	103
Ted	99	TRAVACO	77	VETRA	67	ÅLESUND	21
TELSTAR	83	TRIKS	69	VICTORIA	98		
Tenax	85	TRIODEN	103	Victoria	102	Ägir	81
Tender Commander	22	Troilö	105	VIDAR R	41		
Tender Fighter	22	Troll	79	VIDAR VIKING	30	Öresund	65
Tender Searcher	12	Troms Falken	25	VIIKARI	57		
TENNESSEE	33	Troms Skarven	25	VIKING AVANT	6	ØY-KRAFT	79
TEODORS SPADE	68	Troms Supporter	26	VIKING DYNAMIC	6	ØYVÅG	79
TERRY	77	Troms Titan	25	VIKING ENERGY	6		
TERTTU	51	TROMSFJORD	28	Viking Fighter	22,23		
Teuvo	106	Trønderhav	19	VIKING NAJA	34		

Back cover : The SŁON seen at speed on the approach to Gdansk on 6 August 2003.

(Dominic McCall)